M000202040

Hope you enjoy :

Brush

PROVEN STRATEGIES TO MAKE YOU
AND YOUR DENTAL BUSINESS SHINE

James Goolnik BDS MSc

Brush: Proven strategies to make you and your dental business shine

Published 2011 by Bow Lane Limited.

Printed in Great Britain by Philtone Printing Ltd., Bristol.

Cover design by Atholl McDonald and set by Two Associates

Editing, typesetting and layout by Tom Boyle: tomboyleeditorial.com

ISBN 978-0-9568332-0-4

A CIP catalogue record for this book is available from the British Library.

© James Goolnik 2011

This book is dedicated to Harry and Kate

Love, be loved and never stop learning

4   Brush

Acknowledgments

The people who have had the greatest impact on my life and encouraged me to dream:

My mother Jacqueline who has been the rock of our family and can cook a mean chicken soup.

My father Edward from whom I learnt about business from the age of 5.

My brother Thomas, I'm proud of you.

Harry and Kate, my fabulous children who believe anything is possible.

Thomas Drewry, for your unreserved friendship.

Mark Vardon, Sandra Garcia Martin, Chris Barrow, Manrina Rhode and Dell Goodrick, for reviewing my manuscript. Trent

Smallwood, Cathy Jameson, Dennis Wells and Newton Fahl for being my gurus.

My Entrepreneurs' Organization buddies Daniel, Evan, Eliot, James and Julia.

Vivienne my loyal nurse and the rest of the outstanding team at Bow Lane Dental Group.

All my teachers, colleagues and patients past and present; your contribution to my life and this book have been immense. To Laila, Lydia, Van, Newton, Simon, Mike, Hugh and Pam who have shared your stories and helped me with the statistics. I hope I have done you proud.

Mindy Gibbins-Klein, for giving me the structure to complete the book. Tom Boyle, my editor, for seeing potential in this book and editing and laying it out so professionally. Atholl McDonald, for the illustrations, his tennis tips and helping me with the cover.

Finally I want to thank you, the reader, for having the ambition and drive to want to fulfil your potential. I hope that this may inspire you to help others as well.

Introduction

Fill your paper with the breathings of your heart
William Wordsworth

First things first. I am a clinical dentist. I have worked in universities, hospitals, NHS practice and now in private practice. I studied for my undergraduate degree at King's College London and my master's degree at the Eastman Dental Institute in London; I now teach. At university I joined various dental organisations and got more and more involved in moulding their future. When the time came it was a natural progression to become president of the student body and help forge alliances with other universities. After qualifying I spent a year as a surgical house officer in a hospital, removing difficult wisdom teeth, repairing fractured jaws and putting people's faces back together after they'd had a few too many drinks. My next position was a house officer in a periodontal department, where I got my first glimpse of teaching with the hygiene students. Then it was off into practice to find my fortune—at least that's what I thought.

I worked in NHS and mixed practices learning how to fix people's teeth, often with insufficient time and a box of expired composites. One day I spotted an ad in a dental journal for a forward-thinking dentist to help set up a private practice in the City of London. The owner, Dr. Gregory Belok, had three practices in the US and wanted to set one up in London. We had three long telephone interviews and when we finally met we hit it off straight away. I had the honour of helping to set up a five surgery squat practice from scratch without having any financial responsibility. It was a unique practice in that we specialised in treating the Japanese community in the UK. All the support team were Japanese and I started to learn Japanese. I soon became fluent in asking "Which tooth hurts?" and "Please spit out into the bowl". Not much use in my local Japanese restaurant, though! I was involved with hiring all the team and other dentists as needed.

Once the practice was running smoothly and profitably I decided to further my training and study for a master's degree in conservative dentistry (fixed prosthodontics). I had a mortgage and girlfriend to support so I decided to study part-time. One advantage of this was that it allowed me to keep in touch with what patients actually wanted. Once I completed the master's, having made all my own laboratory work, I realised that I could not carry on practising the sort of dentistry I wanted without having a dental lab on-site. I found a master technician, Mr. Anthony Laurie, took the plunge and set up Bow Lane Dental from a derelict architects' office in the City of London. We now have six treatment operatories with every dental specialist under one roof.

In these pages I share stories of my successes and failures and what I have learned during the ten years I have spent building Bow Lane into one of the highest profile dental practices in the UK, not least through our internet presence on iTunes, YouTube, LinkedIn, Facebook, Foursquare and MSN.

In 2009 I was honoured to be voted president of the British Academy of Cosmetic Dentists, the second largest cosmetic dental organisation in Europe. I have been fortunate to teach in over ten different countries and have personally trained more than 300 dentists and hygienists through my hands-on courses. I often get asked to mentor young dentists and that led me to think 'What better way to start conversations and learning than through a book?'

When I first mentioned writing a book, some said "Go for it." Others said "What have you got to say that anyone would want to hear?" Some said that everything about dentistry had already been written. I disagreed. *My* take on the world of dentistry hadn't been written. The book you are holding is the outcome of that debate. The fact that you have made the effort to beg, borrow, steal or actually buy a copy is vindication enough for me.

The brush is one of the least costly, lowest-tech devices known to dentistry. Paradoxically, it is also the most valuable. According to the Lemelson-MIT Invention Index, the toothbrush was selected as the number one invention that people could not live without.[1] I will be showing you how simple, often free, tools can add the kind of value to your practice that you never thought possible. This book is one such tool. Full of practical tips and advice, hopefully you will find that like the humble toothbrush its value far outweighs its cost. Whether you are a member of a dental team, thinking of setting up on your own, or already run your own dental practice, *Brush* will help you and your business to shine.

What I have written in these pages comes from the heart. I don't believe in holding back, and this is my authentic self. What I have to say may not be to everyone's taste, but I'm reminded of how the comedian Jack Dee got his big break. He trained at the Comedy School and was booked for a series of ten gigs after the course. He really tried to engage with the audience but found that the harder he tried the fewer laughs he got. After his eighth gig he told the promoter he'd had enough. The promoter insisted that he complete the last two gigs or he wouldn't be paid. So with a heavy heart Jack went on stage and delivered the same material with a deadpan face and monotone voice. To his surprise, the audience loved it. The less he tried, the bigger the laughs. He'd found his true authentic self and was not trying to be someone he was not.

One of the lessons of Jack Dee's story is the importance of change. The winners are the ones who accept change and embrace it. The pace of change in dentistry today means that techniques are superseded very rapidly, and the skills you possessed at graduation are no longer sufficient to sustain a lifetime in practice. Change brings opportunity, and wow! have we got an opportunity. Our patients want beautiful healthy smiles but over a quarter of them are terrified to visit us—and it's ALL our fault.

Why's that, you ask?

Contents

Be a business owner and avoid a heart attack

Rich people have small TVs and big libraries. Poor people have small libraries and big TVs.
Zig Ziglar

The owner, the boss, the big cheese, the head kahuna—is that the pinnacle? My parents taught me to have the freedom to run my life how I wanted, do the hours I wanted and have no-one to moan to if it was not how I expected.

I LOVE running my own business. I'm as passionate about dentistry as I ever have been but now I run it for the fun and excitement of meeting new people and the day-to-day challenges rather than the money. Don't get me wrong, I need the money for the school fees and the mortgage, but I would never do what I do just for the financial rewards. As an associate dentist you can make as much money as a principal but go home at 5pm and not think about your job again until 8.30am the next morning. That would bore me, and perhaps you too?

Life as a practice owner is dynamic and fast paced, especially at the beginning. There is a lot of ego invested. Are you doing it because all your friends have a business and you think it is about time? Explore your reasons for starting a business.

A common tale within dentistry is that we have the highest level of alcoholism and suicide of all the professions. The literature does not support this. Do we really believe that dentists are more stressed than police officers, lawyers or paramedics? In reality, there is no compelling evidence that dentistry is an exceptional case.[2] Much of the stress that dentists experience is self-inflicted and a product of acting out their personal ambition. One study speculated that female physicians are more suicide-prone at the beginning of their careers and in midlife, suggesting a problem with the dynamic between being family providers and health care providers. Are female dentists more susceptible to stress-related suicide, as female physicians appear to be?

One survey[3] looked at how dentists dealt with stress:

- 24% of the dentists did nothing
- 32% said they used physical activity
- 13% reported they just "coped"
- Only 10% said they took any time off from practice, and only 6% had a hobby

The American Dental Association (ADA) found over half of all dentists in the US experience pain in parts of their body, most commonly in their lower back and neck.[4] Not a great indication of the health of dentists.

I reduced my risk by not drinking alcohol, not wearing ties and getting rid of all sharp objects in the house! In my opinion dental care professionals get stressed because they feel they are not in control of their own destiny, treat patients who do not want to be there, and work with a team of moaners. To mitigate that stress they drink, overeat and don't look after themselves.

I firmly believe in a healthy mind and healthy body. Your mind and your body need regular nurturing and attention. There are no shortcuts. It's your destiny, you CHOOSE to be stressed or not. Get rid of all your moaning patients and friends, have a clear-out. Moaners tend to attract other moaners. One reason I like moving house every four or five years is you have a chance to get rid of all things that may be useful one day and all the clothes that might eventually come back into fashion.

Declutter your wardrobe, your friends and your patients. As a team we sit down once a month and usually eject at least one patient. In most cases it's because they have been abusive to one of the team members. Life's too short for fussing and fighting. They'll be happier at another practice. We'll be happier too.

A recent ADA survey showed the average net income of a dentist was $230,920 (£144,000); for a specialist the figure was $342,270 (£214,000).[5] The figures show an upward trend in income and a downward shift in the ages of the dentists. The majority of full-time dentists worked an average of 1,928 hours per year. Allowing for six weeks holiday per year, that works out at just under 42 hours a week. I think it is almost impossible to do those hours long-term as a clinical dentist and enjoy a balanced life.

The majority (84%) of all independent dentists work in a practice with just one dentist (them) so it can be lonely. Only 14% of these are women, though every year there is a slow global shift in feminisation of dentistry. In the UK in 2009, 204 more female dentists were added to the Dentists Register than males.[6]

Traits of owner

Over the years I have met thousands of business owners and some of them do have a life outside their business. Among the successful ones I keep coming across similar traits. You may notice a few of them in yourself:

- Passion and a thirst for growth. You can see it in their eyes. They believe in what they are doing. They have a dogged determination. You need to believe in the story before you tell anyone else. So what is your story and why should I be interested in it?

- Self confidence and a willingness to take risks. I'm not talking about the guy who plays poker on a Saturday night or buys lottery tickets. But I don't think you can invest in a business if you are not comfortable taking risks. You can mitigate the level of risk by doing your research, not over-exposing yourself financially, keeping the day job (more of that later) and buying into an existing business. BUT it is still a risk.

- Creativity. They constantly look for better ways to do things. Perhaps you see a gap in the market, or work in a clinic where opportunities are missed and want to explore the possibilities for yourself.

  When I set up Bow Lane I realised there was no exclusive dental practice in the City of London that gave patients what they wanted—good quality dentistry focusing on their needs, using technology to their benefit, backed up by outstanding customer service. I listed all the companies I liked, broke down why I liked doing business with them and then introduced those features to the practice. Would you want to be kept waiting in a shabby waiting room and treated like a number by someone who thinks a bit of pain never hurt anybody? Or would you prefer to wait in a comfortable patient lounge before being treated by someone who is genuinely interested in your condition and how they can help you? More of this later.

- People skills. To get a business off the ground you need help and advice from a lot of different people. To get the most out of them and not be ripped off, taking the time to build a rapport goes a long way. Just as you need to develop a rapport quickly with your patients, you need to have this skill with all the people you deal with.

Don't worry, you do not need to have all these traits yourself. More and more I am seeing business owners who realise they may be missing some of these qualities and then delegate them to a critical person in their team, someone who has the missing skill.

The key to a great business is to focus on your core strengths and delegate the rest. I know you can clean windows, but it is not good use of your time when you could be doing things that only you have the ability to do, such as forging alliances with allied businesses.

You may be thinking of entering a partnership, whether it is an existing one or not. A business partnership has often been referred to as a marriage with no sex. You will spend more time at work than you do at home. No matter how good friends you may be, insist on a written agreement (you'll probably never look at it again unless it goes wrong). It does not need to be a 50-page epic, but it does need to specify:

1. Exactly what is expected of each partner in terms of both financial contributions and contributions to the work of the business.

2. When and how the profits of the partnership will be split.

John set up a seminar business with two friends from his home town, Mark and Phil. They had known each other all their lives but still made a simple agreement of who would have what equity in the business. Two years on, Mark met the woman of his dreams and spent six months following her around the globe. He was not involved in the business and followed his heart. The other two then bought him out the business, valued his shares and sent him a cheque. The business started to lose direction and a year later Phil got bored and started a new venture. John discovered a new concept, wrote a book and the business now was successful again. Phil then got interested in the business again and wanted to sell his share, even though he had had no input in the new business. John was not bitter, just paid him off, but felt his friendship had been abused. The relationship will never be the same.

Insist on a contract, no matter how good friends you are. You never know what will happen! If it does go wrong:

1. Stay calm and try to stay amicable

2. Be willing to compromise

3. Put everything in writing, including the final agreement

4. Make sure you agree what will happen if you/they fail to comply with the exit agreement

5. When it is all over, look back and learn what worked and what didn't for next time!

Matthew ran a stationery company; he wanted to expand it regionally but needed money. He brought in two investors and gave them seats on the board. They did not want Matthew to spend all the money at once and not in the areas Matthew wanted to invest in. It then took him three years to get enough money to buy them out and regain control of the business.

Remember there is no such thing as free money. When somebody wants to lend to you, find out what their key motivator is. Is it financial rewards? If so, how much and by when? Do they want recognition or just to tell their friends they own a dental practice? Are they bored and want a new challenge?

Usually when someone lends you money they either want:

a)   Regular interest on their money. The riskier the project, the higher the returns they are looking for.

b)   Ownership of part of your business (equity). You want to fight for every percentage.

Evaluate what they bring to the table. Is it just money or have they run businesses before? Are they offering expert advice, support and access to their contacts?

Timing of ownership

So you're going to do it. When is the right time? On the day I signed the lease for Bow Lane I also moved into my house in London (I should call it a project as the builders were in for six months). The next day I badly injured my knuckle trying to stop a water leak in the bathroom. A one-handed dentist is not much use to anyone! Life goes on and believe it or not, some of it is beyond your control. For me, having a stable comfortable place to come home to after a long day is very important. Human beings are great at handling change but we all need a certain amount of stability.

You may be thinking about further qualifications. Do you want to be a specialist? Get your studying out of the way first. It is much better to focus on one thing and do it well than do two things badly. Once you qualify you may decide on a different type of practice, as all learning tends to give you a different perspective on life. Your thirst for knowledge may drive you to a postgraduate degree. Only 9% of all the registered dentists in the UK are recognised specialists.[6]

There is no hurry—the average age of a dental graduate in the USA is 29 and 25 in the UK, and 70% of them end up in private practice. The UK produces over 950 newly qualified dentists every year. **I firmly believe that you can do anything you focus on if you want it badly enough.** With the power of the internet it has never been easier to try new hobbies, to network or to find information.

So when is right? Getting your finances in order is a critical step in the timing. One of the tools I used was to list all my current assets and liabilities. That will give you an idea of what you can use as collateral against any loan you may require. It also gives you what your current monthly outgoings are. At this stage you may want to revisit these liabilities and see if you need them all. That satellite TV subscription or that sports car may be able to be traded down to get you closer to your dream.

Part of your business plan should be an estimate of the investment needed to buy into an existing business or set up a new one. How are you going to get access to this money? Do you have an existing relationship with a bank or finance house? They will be impressed if you have a well thought-out plan showing:

- How much you need. Especially critical is the percentage of the loan, i.e. how much of your own money you plan to invest.

- What the money is going to be used for. If it is for equipment, will the loan be paid off before the end of the natural lifespan of the equipment?

- A realistic timescale. Financiers love three-years accounts; crucially, they are looking for consistency and ideally growth over these three years.

They are looking to get their loan paid back, so are you prepared to put money up front or guarantee assets against the loan? Try not to put any guarantees as you could end up losing both your home and your business.

Steven set up a successful lab, he found larger premises and was seduced by the sales reps and easy access to money. He always wanted a Corian top and stainless steel cabinetry, after all wasn't he worth it? Do you think his clients cared about the Corian tops? NO. When things got tight he could not keep up the monthly payments and the bank repossessed his house. Suddenly he was staying at his daughter's house, desperately trying to bail out his business.

So if you have not already got it, start a relationship with a lender. Arrange a meeting. I find private banks much more flexible. Dentistry is a stable profession and they love dentists as customers—they actually pay their loans back! The advantage of a private bank like Coutts is that their bank managers tend not to move on too often so you get to know one another. I remember I was trying to get a residential mortgage (I told you I move a lot) at the start of the recession. Nobody was lending. Coutts agreed a mortgage in principle within two weeks and when I found the property they were able to arrange a surveyor on the day my offer was accepted. Try doing that in your high street bank.

So you have found your ideal practice. The next question is when to hand in your notice. I always think it is better to tell your boss yourself what is going on rather than have them find out on their own. I would suggest being honest and trying to work out a timescale that will allow you to keep working a few regular days so that you maintain an income while setting up the new office. They will appreciate it better if they have time to transfer your patients and find your replacement. As long as the new locations is not too close and there is no direct competition, then you may be able to work part-time for a few months while your new clinic grows. One thing you should not skimp on is getting your new reception up and running. From day one you need a member of your team answering the phone full time to give the impression you are working full time, even if you are not open and the builders are still in. The calls can be diverted to a mobile phone if necessary.

It's OK not to be a business owner

Owning your own business may not be for you. You may have other aspirations; you love dentistry but always wanted to be a crime writer. There are now over one million books published every year (though most sell fewer than 100 copies). You may want to concentrate on bringing up your family and spend as much time as possible watching your children grow up. Work/life balance is important. Let me tell you now, in the first two years of ownership the balance is definitely tipped in favour of the business. It does come back when you have the right team in place and get used to delegating, something that dentists often find difficult to do. But remember: YOU control your journey, nobody else does. What do YOU want to do with it? You can always change you mind at any time. It may not be the right move just now—maybe you always wanted to climb Everest or learn how to cook or write that novel—but it may be next year.

Finding an existing practice to buy

The right opportunity may not have come up. You may be thinking about buying a run-down practice and renovating it. You can increase the chances of an opportunity coming up in various ways:

1. Sign up to a firm of practice brokers. Then meet them and make sure they remember you. Call at least once a month and ask what's new. They will then have you in the back of their mind when the right practice comes up for sale.

2. Decide on which location and what type of practice you want to own. Then plot the existing practices on the map. This may lead you to spot a location that does not have the sort of practice you have in mind. This may be the perfect place to set up a squat practice.

3. Using your map of existing practices, find out as much as you can about them. Ideally you want to know:
   - Name of owner
   - Number of chairs
   - Type of dentistry offered, including any specialties
   - Insurance, public or private model
   - Price list

   You can get your information from all types of sources. I remember a couple of years after I opened I got a call from my architect to say the plans for a dental practice half a mile from me had been approved and it would be opening in three months. By the way, if you already own a practice please do this as well. It is fascinating and will often show you a gap in your market.

   Then write to them. You can use this letter as a template:

[Private and confidential]

Dear Mr X,

I am working with a group of investors who are interested in the dental sector. If you are considering selling your practice within the next 12 months, please contact me on X for a confidential chat about the future.

Yours truly,

You will probably find that about 20% will call you. You can then arrange a chat over coffee, probably away from the practice or out of hours when the team have gone home. I saw over 25 practices this way. You will both benefit from a deal that does not involve agents' fees, but make it clear that you have other opportunities and will need to see all the accounts before you sign anything.

4. Dental reps. They visit scores of practices and often hear when someone is looking to sell or is having financial difficulties. It is always worth letting them know you are looking for opportunities, but make it clear that you don't want your principal to find out.

Benefits of buying an existing business

Some people think it is less risky to buy an established business. You generate revenue from day one, and equipment and staff are already in place. If you choose this route, it is very important to check the contracts of all the staff, especially the self-employed associates and hygienists. It often happens that on a change of ownership they will leave and join a rival practice or set up on their own. Without a robust contract in place they could take valuable patients away.

There may be a number of systems that the practice already uses. They may not work very well but at least they have a history, and often banks feel safer with an existing business with accounts. The business will already have a reputation and that is something you would want to research quite carefully with local people and businesses. Don't rely on the owner or the selling agent to inform you of their reputation. You should expect all the relevant planning permissions and building certificates to be present and correct. If not, that is a good reason to start negotiating the price down. You should also retain part of the purchase money until all outstanding approvals are in place.

📖 Recommended reading: Roger Dawson, The Secrets of Power Negotiation

Brush strokes:

- Why do you want your own business?

- Declutter your wardrobe, your friends and your patients

- Check you have written agreements with business partners and ALL team members

- List your assets and liabilities

- Start/develop a relationship with your bank

- Plot existing practices on a large map

- Find out all you can about the practices

2 Time, money and karma

Money can't buy you happiness but it does bring you a more pleasant form of misery.
Spike Milligan

So you've decided—you are going to do it. When is the best time? Do you wait until your horoscope says everything is perfectly aligned and you have paid off your car loan? Certain things are outside your influence, so what can you get ready in advance? Your minimum checklist should include:

- Business plan—what do I believe?
- SWOT analysis—Strengths, Weaknesses, Opportunities and Threats. Always good to revisit this to spot any weaknesses in your plan.

- Who else do you need in the project—are any key people missing?

Outside influences can affect your timescale.

If you have decided to set up a new practice, you will need an architect to help plan the best use of the building, comply with regulations, optimise the flow of the building work and of course add the wow factor. How do you find the right one?

- Ask colleagues, especially ones who have a practice with a design that you like. Find out who they used.

- Check out trade shows and exhibitions. Architects' firms often have stands at these.

- Talk to dental equipment suppliers. They often work closely with architects to install their equipment.

I DON'T WISH TO TELL THE DENTIST HIS BUSINESS, BUT IS NOW THE RIGHT TIME TO BE GAMBLING ONLINE

Once you have a shortlist, ask to see examples of their work. Don't just look at photographs and drawings. Physically go to their practices. Ask the team, if they could do the project again what elements of the design and layout would they change? Often what looks great on the drawings is not that comfortable to work in. I remember when I set up my first practice the architect put the sterilisation area in the staff room. It was awful. The room had no windows, poor ventilation and was always hot. It was bad because both uses of the room were compromised. A few months later we installed proper ventilation and converted it into the full time sterilisation room. Remember that people do not like working in rooms with no natural light. If you have no choice, you may be able to fit a fake window with artificial lighting to give the illusion of outside light. If that is the only option, be sure that whoever works in the room does not have to spend all day in there!

A good architect will be busy; they will let you know when they are free to start your project. They should give you a timetable so you know how long each stage will take. This will enable you to plan when you need each part of the construction team on site and help you to organise your cash flow.

The same process applies to solicitors. Make sure you have a plan so that all the contracts are in place and the lease is in order when you need them.

From the previous chapter you may have identified an area of the country which is missing your type of dental practice. How do you find the right location? You could register will all the commercial estate agents and trawl through all the ads in online and printed media. In my opinion that is waste of your valuable time. Hire a professional! When I set up Bow Lane I used Richard Proctor of CBRE. I gave him the ideal specification and location for my business and he went to work. He shortlisted six locations and the one I chose was under offer by another dentist. What a small world. He made a bid on my behalf as a commercial agent and outbid the other dentist! If I'd gone in on my own, the landlord would have sold to the other party. People respect knowledge and track records, and that was what I was paying for.

Don't forget it's not all about you. You obviously have been talking about your project with your partner. It may be you are going to give up your job while the practice is being built and you both need to live off your partner's income. This all needs to be discussed. Is this the best time in their career? Maybe they are about to go for promotion and need you to wait until their own position is clear.

There is also market timing to think about. 2008 marked the start of the biggest worldwide recession since 1929 and at the time of writing—early 2011—the future is still uncertain. Is this the best time to open a new business? I say YES. As long as you have done your homework, worked out your cash flow and the numbers using the worst case scenario, then go for it. I think conditions like this represent an amazing opportunity; you are more likely to get good deals as you are bucking the trend and building when others are shrinking. What is crucially important is that your business plan is robust, as the hardest thing in a recession is access to money. The lenders are backing people and teams. Have you got the right expertise on board, and have you planned for the worst?

As well as conditions in the money market, you also need to look at trends in the market for dentistry. There is a definite shift away from cosmetic spa practices towards more conservative full service practices. Orthodontics is growing massively, especially since the advent of invisible braces and 'fast' orthodontics like the Inman Aligner. The days when you cut down twelve healthy teeth and placed veneers on them are long gone.

Running out of cash is a sin

How many times have you heard cash is king? Well, it is. Do you know the definition of bankruptcy? If you answer yes to the following question you could be bankrupt and trading illegally, depending on the law in your country:

- Have you reached a point where the current bills (liabilities) are larger than the cash (liquid assets) you have in the bank?

- If all your creditors wanted to be paid TODAY, could you pay them? I have to admit that there have been lots of times in my career when I couldn't have paid them all at once, especially just after paying a large tax bill.

Prioritise your spending. This is one of the most important lessons I have learnt. When I set up Bow Lane it was designed as a four surgery practice. I completely fitted out two rooms ready to go. The remaining two rooms had all the electrics and plumbing in place but no equipment or cabinetry. We call this the first fix only. It meant I would instantly save about £10,000 per room; it also meant I had time to see how I got on with the equipment in the other rooms and whether I wanted to duplicate it. It's similar when you move into a new house and live in it for a few months to work out how best to use the space.

I firmly believe it is more effective to use one single supplier of cabinets and chairs for the entire practice. It is easier to swap parts when bits break, and the team have a less steep learning curve in how to maintain them. It is also easier for the clinicians to switch rooms and get working. It is easy to be seduced at the showroom by the most expensive chairs with all the extras, just like in a car showroom. But think about it from the patients' perspective—will they perceive the difference in worktop materials? Do they care? NO. Things like digital X-rays are a no-brainer. They are better for the patient and the clinician, and actually save money in the long run—no chemicals, less down time and easier to communicate with colleagues via email.

One of my friends set up a state of the art nine-surgery practice. It had everything and as money was easy they decided to fit out all nine surgeries in one go, even though at the time there were only four dentists in the practice. Before they were able to get the other five rooms busy they had run out of funds. In the end the bank repossessed the building.

Draft a budget

I know it's boring. Try to find someone who finds Excel exciting. If you do not know anyone, then ask your accountant to do it. The most important aspect, if you do not do this yourself, is to make sure that whoever is doing it is thoroughly briefed. Once they have produced a spreadsheet, get them to go through it with you so you understand it and know where to put the income and expenses. Make sure you use realistic figures and try inputting worst case scenarios so you can at least cover the first 12 months' operating costs. Once this is done, it should be a living document. Keep updating it, adding the real figures and seeing changes to the bottom line. It should not be a one-off exercise for the bank; it will help you read the pulse of your business.

I thought I had thought of everything. I have an investment property for which I received a monthly rental. The existing tenants decided they wanted to stay on another year so we agreed an increase in rent and carried on as normal. I checked my account about a week after the rent should have gone in and it was nowhere to be seen. I emailed the tenants who said it was a bank error. By the time I actually received the rent it was a month later. Could your cash flow model cope with a situation like this or would it put your account overdrawn? I would allow for a degree of cushion, especially dealing with builders. I think a 20% contingency on top of the building quote is sufficient to allow for unforeseen circumstances. If they don't happen, then you have some extra working capital.

What needs to be in your budget?

- Projected income—look at your past performance and knock off 25% to be prudent.

- Lab bills—about 11% of overhead.

- Material bills—about 6% of overhead. You can get really generous discounts when setting up a new clinic by ordering the majority of materials from one supplier. The other thing to negotiate is when you have to pay them (terms of credit). They want your business and you may be able to arrange a deal where you pay only 25% of the invoice on receipt and the remainder over the following three months.

- Staff wages—about 17.5% of overhead. These are the first people to pay, even if you have cash flow issues. They are the lifeblood of your business they need to be 100% sure of being paid.

- Dentist salaries, if you have others working for you. The tradition of paying an associate 50% of the gross fees is long dead. If they want to work in a cutting-edge practice with excellent materials, highly motivated and trained staff, you are looking at 35%.

- Rent and rates. With a new lease you can often negotiate a rent-free period. We got six months on a 14-year lease. Try to get this period to start on the first day of trading and not the day you sign the lease as the fit-out time will eat into this.

- Printing and stationery. With the speed of reordering I try to keep my stationery stock as low as possible. It goes out of date very quickly. All my patient communications are also online to keep costs down, increase efficiency and allow for constant tweaking, for example new patient welcome packs, medical histories and recalls.

- Communications. How much you expect to spend on phones, including text reminders.

- Computers. Look at the scale of the overall project and ensure you get a server that will be up to the job for at least three years. Install workstations only as needed.

- Software. Include not only the cost of purchasing the licenses but also any support costs, including a robust back-up solution both on-site and off-site.

- Professional fees. Try to get a fixed cost from all your advisors as fees can mount up rapidly.

- Finance costs. These include not only loan repayment costs but also bank charges. You should be able to get free banking for at least one year, especially if you play one bank off against another. Dentistry is one of the safest businesses, and the banks want your custom. Don't forget the credit card charges for each transaction and the monthly terminal rental.

A well managed practice has a practice overhead of 55-65%. The individual ratios will depend on what type of dentistry you offer.[7]

Protect your primary source of income

I know many dentists who have become so excited by a new project that they take their eye off the day job that was paying all the bills. The rest of the team can notice this and start to feel neglected. Before you know it your profits are down and you have a battle to improve morale. Make sure you ringfence your livelihood. If you need to take some days off work, then factor that into the equation. When the time is right, explain the project to your team but make sure they know your priority is still your existing practice. There are a few high profile dentists who get carried away with their success and start opening more branches. Whenever they are in the building everything goes well and the team appear happy but immediately they are gone, the team's punctuality starts to suffer and sometimes they do not turn up at all. Stock control and ordering goes awry. Result—a complicated mess. In my experience one well run and motivated practice can make more money than multiple sites, and cause less stress. It helps if you have an excellent business manager, but you still need to show great leadership qualities. A leader is someone who inspires others to also be leaders.

Are you working on or in your business?

When I set up Bow Lane I was working as a full-time associate dentist for another practice. I cut my workload down to three days per week while I built up Bow Lane with the help of Christine, my part-time hygienist. I had a full time receptionist taking calls and once I was busy on those two days, I gave my notice in and worked full time. Ten years on, I have cut down to work three days per week clinically and one day to run the business. For me it is the perfect balance and allows me to be authentic in all areas of my life. A recent survey showed 15% of dentists in the US work five days per week and 44% work a four-day week.[8]

It must fit in with your painted picture

What are you career aspirations? Do you want to teach in a hospital? Do you want to be an international lecturer in periodontology? Where do you see yourself in three years from now? Three years is far enough to make things achievable without putting yourself under stress.

I was at a seminar where Cameron Herold used a tool called the 'painted picture'. You imagine it is three years from now and you have just got on a plane to go to your favourite holiday destination; you sit down next to an old friend whom you have not seen in three years. The friend is excited to see you again and asks what you have been up to.

The best way to produce this picture is to move away from your normal environment to somewhere you will feel inspired. Get away from your computer—you will tempted to check your emails and be brought back into current issues. Don't focus on the how. Just get a large piece of paper—A3 is ideal—and sketch it out. I was fortunate enough to sit next to Tony Buzan at a dinner and was inspired by his story of how he developed the idea of mind mapping in the 1970s. Mind maps are visual representations of the thought process and help you to visualise, structure and classify ideas. I find just putting words down on paper makes your thinking much clearer. Be as descriptive as possible. It's your life—what would you say?

Once you have this map it should be easy to formulate your vision for three years from now. Make sure you include every area: team, marketing, sales, operations, customer service, finance etc.

You need to imagine that you are walking into your practice three years from now. What do you see? What are patients saying about your practice? What is the team talking about in the staff room? What does your day look like? What treatments are you carrying out? What are your plans for the evening? Think about it NOW and WRITE it down. Studies repeatedly show that writing your thoughts down and then sharing them with your close friends make them more likely to happen. It makes you accountable.

Your vision document will probably fill three pages. Re-read and refine it. Once you are happy with it, share it with your team. It will help them understand their role and whether this is the sort of practice they would love to be associated with. Once you have your plans, don't just bury them away in your desk. Take them out at least every month and read them out loud. Do they still excite you? Perhaps you have changed your mind. Tweak and revisit your painted picture regularly.

I would suggest you reread it at every strategic planning session so the entire team are engaged (more about this in Chapter Four). See if is coherent and whether it needs tweaking to fit with the current team members and the delivery of dental services.

Do you need a coach?

Think about what you enjoy doing. Are there any people out there who have your ideal job? My view is that finding a role model or mentor is critical. Cultivate their friendship. In my experience successful people enjoy sharing their tips for success with enthusiastic, respectful students. They remember their path and love to share the stories. How did they get where they are today, what was the one thing they know now that they did not know when they were like you? If you are lucky they may offer to be your coach or mentor. It gives you accountability and helps you steer in the right direction. Why make the same mistakes twice when you have someone's experience to guide you along the path. I have used coaches throughout my career. I find them invaluable.

Don't worry about what they do; it is all about what they say. Many successful coaches talk about work/life balance, but just take a look at their life! Anything but balanced. I still think you can learn a lot from these people. Sign up for at least six months and at the beginning write down what you want to have achieved at the end of that time. These are your desired outcomes. It may be to set up a clinic on your own, expand your business to another surgery or increase your profitability by 10%. Make these goals SPECIFIC and MEASURABLE so you know if you have achieved them.

Share them with your coach and draw up an action plan to get there. I remember one great tool I used was when I sent a weekly email update to my coach. There were just three simple questions on this form:

a) what went well

b) what went badly

c) what I need help with

I actually don't remember him actively helping me much. What was really invaluable was the process of having to sit down to analyse my previous week. We are very bad at celebrating the successes in our lives; it is very easy to focus on what we have not achieved yet.

For example, list the top five things you are proud of achieving in the last year. This is not a book on goal setting but I use the 'Wheel of Life' to help identify areas where I may want to focus my attention. This is one of the tools that can be used to get a snapshot and identify the first steps on your journey to success.

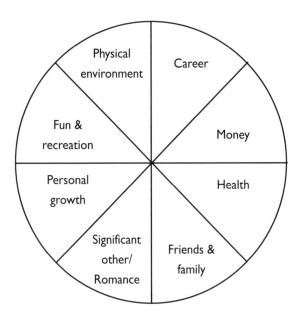

Assign a number from 1 to 10 next to each category, write 1 if you are unsatisfied in this area and up to 10 if you are totally satisfied.

Look at the scores: what are the two lowest scores? What are the two highest scores? What are the two areas you would most like to move forward?

How would you feel if you could significantly move forward in these two areas? What could you do NOW to start moving forward in these areas?

Once I have filled all sections in, I then set an overall theme for the year. For me this year is 'Building the brand and fatherhood'. What would yours be? Do you want to leave a legacy—what would you like to be remembered for? I put them in my organiser or phone and when I have a quiet moment I take a quick look at them and tick them off. You may find a goal that you put last month doesn't really sound true with you any more. Just rub it off. It's your list!

I have this big magnetic whiteboard in my office. I put my overall annual theme on it and then add individual tasks and goals. I use multicolour pens and stick pictures and cards of things that mean something to me around the board.

It may be a photograph of an evening with good friends, a thank you letter from a patient, tickets to a play I am looking forward to. It motivates me every day just to see it.

It is hard not to get emotional about all this. I implore you to share you dream with as many friends as possible. Authentic people share their dreams, and the more you share the more likely they are to come true. You never know when your friend has a connection that could help you take a step towards one of your goals. A friend of mine, Daniel Priestley, was talking about the book he was writing and I was excited. I had always wanted to write a book but did not know where to start. He put me in contact with his book-writing coach, Mindy Gibbins-Klein, and here we are—my first book in print!

You can only achieve so much at once

Most humans don't like change. It scares them and unsettles them. Have you noticed how many people stay in unhappy relationships just because they are scared of leaving their partners? Do you want to live a life full of regrets? If you accept change, the worst that can happen is you end up saying "I tried and it did not work that time. But I have learnt from it."

Smilestrips

A while ago I noticed a gap in the market in tooth whitening products. Tooth whitening toothpaste did nothing. Kits bought over the counter at the chemist also did nothing. Some even burnt the gums or dissolved the teeth due to their acidity. The only option was to go to the dentist and get bespoke whitening trays at a cost of over $250 (£155). In the USA there was a product called Whitestrips that sold for about $30 and actually worked, albeit on just the front teeth. I found a manufacturer in China to design a larger version, called them Smilestrips and started selling to dentists. I then ran into two problems, one due to the high peroxide content and the current law in the EU. I was unable to get a CE mark, which certifies that a product has met European consumer safety, health and environmental requirements. This meant no retailers or practices would touch the product. The second problem was when the strips got above room temperature the peroxide gel would start to run, making the product messy and difficult to apply. I immediately withdrew the product and am now reformulating it to see if we can make it more temperature stable. By then hopefully the EU law will fall in line with the rest of the world. Things do not always go according to your plans. If so, be honest, take a step back and refocus. Don't hide the truth— it will come out in the end.

Mind-body connection

You will find that the most successful people in any profession, if they have been there for a while, have a stable support network to bounce ideas off. They also invest time in having a healthy body. To achieve sustainable change in the long run you need to nurture your body and mind. Having spent years in the gym, it now bores me. You get sick for a week and it takes a month to get back to where you were. I find yoga works the best for me, specifically Bikram yoga (www.bikramyoga.com) as it has a mind-body connection I have not found in other types of yoga. It is the sweaty yoga in the hot room. After about ten classes you don't notice the heat, it helps your flexibility and lessens the chance of injury. Since I have been practising I have had no sporting injuries and it helped heal a fractured wrist and elbow much quicker than the doctors predicted. After I fractured my elbow (motorcycles and dentistry do not mix) the doctors advised no yoga for six weeks and said I would be unlikely to be able to work for about a month. I was in the yoga studio three days later and back at work in five. The heat really helped the healing and stretching the joint, and I now have 100% use of my elbow.

Find out what exercise works for you. It may be swimming or a brisk walk with the dog. Some of my friends find running a way to calm down after a long day and a good opportunity to think.

A balanced diet also goes hand in hand with looking after your body. You cannot expect to achieve your best if you fuel your body on hamburgers and chips. I am not saying don't eat them, but it is all about balance. Getting enough rest and sleep is also vital. There are plenty of books on that subject, so let's move on.

You need focus

If a project is worth doing, you need to direct 100% energy to it. How can you do that if you have your day job that is paying your bills? We talked earlier about looking at your liabilities. I want you to look at the things that defocus you:

- Any medical conditions
- Teeth that need fixing
- House repairs
- Monthly bills
- Watching TV
- Listening to the news

Clear things out of the way, put as much as you can on direct debit or get them out of your life. If you were a bird it would be like preparing your nest for winter. Clear your desk. I am not expecting you to be a monk and not see your friends. When you are working on the project, WORK on the project: turn off phones, internet, TV and get on with it. You will need breaks and then you can spend time on whatever distractions you fancy.

Personally I have not watched TV in two years and I don't miss it. It just saps away your time and doesn't give you much back. I get all my news on the radio in the morning and a weekly update from *The Week* magazine, a great overview of home and world news plus opinions from some of the best writers out there. Most news is negative and there is NOTHING you can do about the latest landslide or famine apart from giving to charity. You come away from the news sad, negative and less trusting of humanity. Why does everyone seem to want to kill everyone? Try a news famine for just a week and see the difference.

Tim Ferriss in the *4-Hour Workweek* talks about outsourcing everything in your life that does not need to be done by you and can be done cheaper and more efficiently by someone else. If you love doing the ironing and it relaxes you, please carry on (I'll send mine round). It bores me to tears and I am rubbish at it!

Ferriss also talks about most people's weekly productivity being distilled down to four hours. If you could achieve the same results and get paid the same, would you not prefer to work four hours instead of the usual 35! It works to some extent in dentistry. If you went through the entire list of patients you saw last week and then worked out which ones actually needed to be seen by you and were productive to treat, you would find:

- Some just wanted advice which could have been administered by the practice nurse, for example dealing with a sore wisdom tooth.

- Some needed referral to a specialist or wanted to discuss orthodontic options.

- Some needed suture removal—a job for a practice nurse or hygienist/ therapist.

- High spot on a filling—again, therapist or hygienist.

- A regular check-up—would that have been better as a hygiene exam in the hygiene room? This is where the dentist comes in for two or three minutes and the hygienist presents the patient. They have a look around the mouth to see if there any issues to be dealt with that need rebooking. If so, at least both the dentist and patient are aware of the problem, the number of appointments needed, the length of those appointments and the fee.

- Tooth whitening—should be done by the hygienist. It's more fun for them and increases their hourly rate. We now offer treatment of tooth sensitivity and caries control. Van

Haywood has shown that using carbamide peroxide in trays is a safe way not only to whiten the teeth but also, by increasing the pH, to stop decay.[9] Trays are also a great way to deliver desensitising agents to the teeth.

- New patient wanting to discuss cosmetic options—wouldn't a treatment coordinator do a better job and build a quicker rapport with the patient?

Actually what DID you do all week?

The business side of dentistry should be run by the business manager and the team rotas worked out by the clinical manager, with the dentist having monthly meetings with these two in order to steer the ship.

In the future I see dentists as the second line of defence. All patients will be triaged by the treatment coordinator who decides which clinician they should see for their specific problem. It may be that they then see the dentist who draws up a treatment plan and supervises the patient's overall specialist care. The dental team will be trained to a specific niche and the patient will see the best person for the job while receiving an overall umbrella of care by the practice.

Brush strokes:

- SWOT analysis

- Have you got the right people?

- Prioritise your spend. What is important to get your business off the ground?

- Negotiate not only a discount but also when you have to pay

- What do you do to stretch your mind?

- Draw your painted picture and share it with your team

- Set goals using the wheel of life

- Try a news famine for a week

- Go through the last week of patients you saw. Which ones actually needed to see you?

3 This is a relationship business

If we keep doing what we're doing, we're going to keep getting what we're getting.
Stephen R. Covey

Let's face it, not many people actually want to go to the dentist. They may want to be free from pain, replace that missing front tooth or have a smile they can be proud of. But they don't want to go through the treatment that produces the end result. Only 53% of the UK population visit the dentist.[10]

That's where we come in. Too many practices spend time and money on all the fluff that makes a trip to the dentist look like a pleasant experience without focusing on what really matters: THE PEOPLE WHO DELIVER THAT SERVICE. If you don't invest time and money in the people, I don't care how great a dentist you are, what fancy new equipment you have, or how your office colours create an oasis of calm and tranquillity. I don't want to be there!

The patient's relationship with the dentist is different. Ask anyone who wears glasses "What is the name of the optician who carries out your eye test?" and the majority would not have a clue. If you ask the same question about their dentist I bet they would all know their name.

You have different relationships with your team members, and they all need to be fed and nurtured with the same degree of care and attention. Obviously each one needs to be handled differently but the underlying message is YOU CARE and YOU ENJOY SPENDING TIME WITH THEM. Otherwise you should fire them and hire someone that you enjoy being with.

Build and maintain that patient relationship

So before we go any further, what is your ideal patient?

Everyone has a different idea of what makes a patient ideal; some characteristics are non-negotiable, like 'pays their bills on time', some may not be important to you, like 'smells nice'. For me, the ideal patient:

- is punctual and informs you if they are running late.
- pays bills on time without hassle.
- is a raving fan—enjoys being in your practice and refers others who also become raving fans. Some practices never need to do any marketing. The raving fans do it for them.
- respects you and other team members—often they are respectful to the clinical team but not to the office staff.
- listens to your clinical advice and then makes an informed decision.
- attends all maintenance and hygiene appointments as prescribed.
- smells nice, knows which end of a toothbrush to use and actually uses it!

How do you get more of them?

Ask. Just ask your existing patient base and as you slowly weed out the sub-prime ones you will eventually be left with a majority of ideal patients. Among these there will be some who fit all the criteria but only attend when they have a mini-crisis. They are to all intents and purposes ideal because when they visit you they follow all your advice and get healthy again, though they usually disappear into the ether until another mini-crisis looms.

A lot of clinicians find asking for referrals quite stressful and wonder what to do if the patient refuses. I have never had this happen, probably thanks to a technique I have developed. It needs a bit of practice, but the following line (or your version of it) tends to work, especially if it is delivered after a course of treatment:

"You know what, Mrs Sandersley, I have really enjoyed taking care of you over the last few weeks. Our practice grows by recommendations from people like you. If you know any family members, friends or colleagues who need treatment I would love to take care of their dental needs. Here are a couple of my business cards."

I would empower all of the clinical team to have this conversation at the end of a course of treatment before the patient goes back into the recare system.

I also believe in the use of referral cards, as pictured opposite. These should encompass the ethos of your practice and establish an emotional connection to what you believe in. They should also discourage the sort of patient behaviour that you want to avoid. I remember we had a patient who would always turn up 10 or 15 minutes late for appointments, huffing and puffing. The clinicians would get stressed in case the next patient had to wait and they ended up running late all day. This was brought to my attention at a practice meeting. So I put a note on the patient's record card and the next time he was due in I made a point of talking to him. As usual he was late, so instead of having him see his regular hygienist I collected him from the patient lounge and took him to my office.

I said that we valued him as a patient but it was impossible to offer him the level of clinical care and customer service in the remaining appointment time available. I told him the clinicians try their best to allow enough time to complete his treatment comfortably, but if he was late that was impossible. So if he wished to remain a patient with us, he had to arrive on time for his

Your referral cards should encompass the ethos of your practice and establish an emotional connection to what you believe in.

appointments. If he was late in future we would be unable to treat him but the full charge for the wasted clinical time would still be due. The alternative was for us to part company and he find a practice that could meet his customer service requirements. He was a little shocked but has been coming back for the past two years, often 15 minutes early!

Sometimes it's a matter of training your patients, but this approach can only work if your team is trained to a similar level.

What happens when it all goes wrong?

I once referred a patient of mine to a colleague on my team for a specific tooth to be treated. I had been treating this patient for the past eight years, along with his wife and management team. He was booked in on a day when the London Underground was on strike so the trains were severely delayed. The patient arrived 15 minutes early and asked if the clinician was there. The front desk team said yes (first mistake). The rest of the team were in and the surgery was ready, but there was no sign of the clinician. He had tried to call to say he was stuck in traffic but the phones were still switched over to the answering service (mistake number 2). They called him and he said he was looking for parking and would be around 15 minutes. At that time he was five minutes late. The patient was told that the clinician was looking for parking and should not be much longer (mistake number 3).

After 25 minutes the patient walked out. The clinician arrived five minutes later. We sent flowers and a card to the patient immediately. The clinician called him the same day, apologised and offered to rebook him along with a discount. They then got into a discussion that the clinician should have got up earlier, knowing there was a strike. The patient said he would think about rebooking and the call ended. The clinician then decided he did not like the patient's attitude and refused to see him again. As the principal I called the patient the next day, he realised it was just a clash of personalities and he would be happy to come back again. When I mentioned him seeing another colleague, he said he would see the original dentist or he would find another practice, which he did.

I lost a large case and an eight-year relationship with the patient, his family and his colleagues, all from a series of silly mistakes.

Try to see things through the eyes of the customer. This patient had made an effort to get to the practice despite a transport strike. He probably hadn't slept well, knowing he was going to the dentist in the morning. He'd had to rearrange his day around the appointment and the possible aftercare. He did not want to hear about the clinician's problems. All he wanted to hear was: "We're sorry, we have taken action to stop the same thing happening again. Let's get your treatment rescheduled at a time that is good for you."

A monopoly going nowhere

An orthodontic lab became the only provider of a removable orthodontic appliance. At first when they were not busy the product was good, service was good and everyone was happy. More and more dentists started using the laboratory. They became too busy, a monopoly that had no room for expansion. The products started to come back late, the technicians weren't reading the prescriptions and therefore producing incorrect appliances. When asked about this, they just said they were busy. If you asked for a job slightly quicker, they said no problem, just double the fee! Within a few months clinicians were going out of their way to get the appliances made abroad, even though it was more inconvenient and involved using FedEx.

People like doing business with people they like and respect. Lose that and you start losing business.

It's only money

My business ethos is that if someone is genuinely not happy with the outcome and you have tried your best, I offer them a full refund as a gesture of goodwill. One of my patients wanted to change their veneers. They were placed ten years ago and had become unsightly and chipped with exposed stained margins. We did all the wax-ups and got them approved and then placed the temporary veneers. The patient was thrilled and we went on to construct the final veneers with our in-house laboratory.

We tried the final veneers and the patient was not sure as she was numb but she thought one was slightly lighter than the others. We cemented them in and asked her to return in a week to review them. One week later she said she had not left the house as they were horrible. I noticed the one which was lighter had not improved and two others I could improve on. We decided to remake these three veneers and made new temporaries. The patient was then not happy with the new temporaries. We came to fit the final three veneers and the colour was spot on now, but she did not like the shapes. I decided not to fit the new veneers and take them all off and start again. She again liked the new temporaries but when the final ones came back she found something else she did not like.

I could not see how I could improve on them. I took photographs and showed them next to her original teeth. She still did not like them. So I said "I am afraid I cannot give you the smile you are looking for", refunded her all the money on condition she signed a disclaimer that it was a gesture of goodwill. I accepted no liability and she could not return as a patient or seek any redress for the dental care I provided.

Some patients you cannot treat, and the earlier you spot them the better.

Don't forget about professional relationships

Whoever you recommend to your patients is a reflection on you. If that bookshop you recommended at the last appointment had a member of staff who was rude to your patient, it reflects badly on you. I only recommend people if I have personally met them.

Say your patient needs their wisdom teeth removed and they would like it carried out under general anaesthesia, so you refer them to an oral surgeon. If the oral surgeon has different diagnostic criteria for removal, it will upset your patient and undermine their confidence in you. I will have met the oral surgeon before I start to refer to him so that I understand what sort of clinic they run, what treatments they offer, their criteria for wisdom tooth removal and the aftercare they offer. This is to make sure everything matches the ethos of my clinic. If I am not sure about a diagnosis I will tell the patient I am not sure and that we are asking for a second opinion. I also tell them what is likely to happen at that initial appointment, including the likely fee.

People do not like strange environments and uncertainty, so we try to reduce the amount of unknowns they will be exposed to and make them feel cared for and important.

You're never off brand!

I meet my future patients in all sorts of weird places—a new year's fancy dress party, a yoga class, at check-in on a flight (I never did get that upgrade from economy!) Are you congruent with your brand, your business ethics and your principles in all your everyday activities? People want to be with authentic people with similar values. If you believe in the mind-body connection through yoga and the other students in the class feel the same way, they will feel a natural bond to you and are more likely to trust their dental care to you. If you show high standards of personal hygiene they assume you also do that in your day job and trust you. And vice-versa, I never understand why people sitting in a traffic jam in their car think the glass is ONE WAY!

In all you dealings with members of your inner circle, you are your brand. You will be referred patients from the most unlikely places, but don't forget to thank the referral source. Make them feel special and appreciated for thinking of you. I always think a hand-written card says a lot and it only takes a few seconds. Have some good quality thank you cards printed and just put a personal note on one and send it to their workplace. People rarely get handwritten letters nowadays. With the rise of electronic communication a personal note really stands out and makes the receiver go WOW.

An amazing 70% of all litigation is related to poor communication.[11] You invest in clinical skills—why not invest in how you and your team communicate? UK dentists are at least twice as likely as their colleagues in the USA and Australia to find themselves under some kind of challenge from their professional regulator, and several times more likely to do so than their colleagues in many other parts of the developed world, including Europe.

A brand is a **promise**. A strong brand is a promise that is **kept**.

Speak like a leader

I think it is important to give back and share with your colleagues, whatever your position. The best way to do that is start with local study clubs and networking meetings where you can stand up and give a ten-minute presentation. I know that most people's worst fear is public speaking, so start with a small audience and choose a topic you love. For example:

1. A case you treated. Show before and after pictures and discuss why you made certain treatment decisions.

2. A marketing campaign.

3. Your mistakes—always goes down well.

4. A new technique you just learned, e.g. minimal preparation veneers.

There are lots of public speaking books and courses available. Two tips I found really helpful were:

a. Don't have too many slides, or too much text on each slide. Your audience will end up reading the slides and not engaging with you. Only put on a slide what you want people to remember, ideally an image that will resonate with them and act as an aide-memoire for you. Their attention should be on you, not your slides. You also need to strike a balance between entertainment and education.

b. You will get nervous, so speak to a few members of the audience before your talk so you see some friendly faces when you get up to speak. Make eye contact with these people from time to time to deliver certain points.

Remember, as Mark Twain said, there are two types of public speakers: those who are nervous before they start, and the liars.

Once you get more confident and in demand you can start charging more than just travelling expenses. I always insist of 50% of my fee up front to reserve my time and gain commitment from the promoter.

I started to do some lecturing and always loved watching stand-up comedy and thought "public performance doesn't get much scarier than that". Imagine standing up in front of a room full of strangers and trying to make them laugh. A patient of mine did just that and said it was one of the most frightening moments in his life. So I thought why not, I like a challenge. I enrolled in the Comedy School in London under the directorship of Keith Palmer. Once a week for seven weeks I sprayed on triple deodorant, spent most of the morning beforehand on the toilet and found a use at last for my Christmas funny socks. It turned out the socks were no use but the course was fabulous. I learnt what makes people laugh. It stems from one of two situations:

1. We feel superior to the comic. "If you can't laugh at yourself, make fun of others." (Bobby Slaton, an American stand-up comic)

2. A surprise that we did not see coming, the twist at the end of the joke. Often used to cover our feelings of embarrassment.

Public at large

What's your public image? You may have appeared in the media—what's your message? Do you have a stock photograph that allows the reader to see what you look like? Is it ten years out of date? Would people recognise you in the street or have you gone to town on Photoshop?

What is your image locally? Get a friend to visit a few local businesses and ask what they know about the local dental office. They may not even know you exist!

Have you or someone in your team been media trained? You may have noticed how the same people in our profession keep reappearing in the media. It's not because they are any smarter than the rest of us. It's because they have grabbed an opportunity and understand how the media works. Once you offer a comment to the media and it is pitched correctly they tend to ask you again.

If you're shy you can outsource this role to one of your team, someone who perhaps likes being in the public eye and finds this kind of thing comes naturally.

So how do you become media friendly?

1. Always think about the piece from the perspective of the listener/viewer/reader. What are their demographics? You need to make your message easy for them to understand. In the trade they call them soundbites—short, snappy bits of information that answer the question and engage with the audience.

2. Remember the majority of the media are trying to make you look good. It is not in the journalist's interest to trip you up (unless you're being investigated).

3. Media people are driven by deadlines. Respect this and always get back to them quickly.

4. Go to a professional to get training. A half day will get you started in how to prepare and how to reply to questions. You get a chance to see yourself on camera, spot those nervous tics you never knew you had, and learn how to control them. Mine was tapping my feet.

📖 Recommended reading: <u>Malcolm Kushner</u>, Public Speaking for Dummies;

These courses are also recommended:

<u>Dale Carnegie Training</u>, High-Impact Presentations

<u>Dr Paul Homoly</u>, Just Because You're an Expert...Doesn't Make You Interesting

Do you need a PR agency?

You can also hire an external agency to manage your entire public relations. They can work with you either on a retainer basis or per project. You may be launching a new clinic and need as much local exposure as possible and decide you want to run a campaign for six months and launch with a bang. You then need to agree a fixed fee for the job, a time scale and what extras will not be covered in this estimate, such as travelling and photocopying.

Alternatively some high profile clinics pay an agency a fixed monthly fee to work with them on an ongoing basis. They have monthly strategy meetings with a progress report and list of press clippings. Please bear in mind it takes at least three months for any campaign to get off the ground and it takes momentum to keep it there. It tends to dry up very quickly afterwards as there often is another practice also vying for the media's attention.

I would definitely recommend that you get your agency to agree to represent only one type of practice, for example an orthodontic clinic in a specific geographic area, to prevent any overlap or competition.

You can do a lot of what an agency does yourself, but is it the best use of your time and do you really have such a good list of health and beauty contacts? If you do in-house PR you can get a list of the health and beauty editors from the front pages of each magazine you want to target. Then call the magazine editorial team and ask for "Sarah Smith's" email and contact number. They are much more likely to give it to you if you ask for the person by name rather than just requesting the beauty editor's details. Every time you send a press release by email follow it up the next day with a phone call.

The key points for a good press release are:

- Make the headline eye-catching and the first sentence interesting or intriguing so that the reader wants to know more.
- Be brief—one sheet of paper, no more.
- Make it worth talking about—have a GREAT story.
- Include your full contact details.

This is not the place to discuss how to write a perfect press release—there are plenty of great websites on the subject. Take a look at www.journalism.co.uk

What about your team?

How do they represent you and your clinic outside work? What do they say when asked what they do? There's a big difference between "I'm a dental nurse" and "I work in a healthcare team and rebuild people's confidence in their smiles."

Do they carry business cards to give to potential new patients? I gave all my team their own business cards with their photographs on. When they meet someone new and they discuss their job they often offer a card because they are passionate about where they work. When you go out for a team away day, offer $10 (or £10) for every team member who has a business card on them. Do this randomly about once a year. They will realise it is in their interest financially to always carry a few business cards!

Do you know why they go to work? For the money, you say. That's strictly not true. Most people work to feel appreciated, though they need the money too. You often hear about practices that pay well above average but have a high staff turnover. They try to compensate for the lack of appreciation by overpaying. It does not work in the long run and if you take a look at Maslow's research in 1943 you can see why.

Maslow developed his Hierarchy of Needs theory and it remains true today for understanding human motivation in terms of management training and personal development. People are motivated by unsatisfied needs. As each of these needs is significantly satisfied, it drives the next need to emerge. The needs are often portrayed in the shape of a pyramid, with the largest and most fundamental needs at the bottom. Good leaders recognise that if they're to build productive and highly successful teams, they need to understand and look after the needs and well-being of team members. You have a whole range of options to help your team, not just money. As a minimum you should have a safe

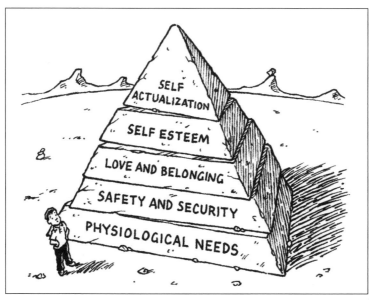

Maslow's Hierarchy of Needs

working environment and team activities—and it costs nothing to say thank you.

One of our unique selling points at Bow Lane is the continuity of our team. The other team members and patients love it. They feel part of a family and it seems that pregnancy is the only reason that people leave. So the men have no chance!

Do you help to nurture their personal and professional development? Are they happy in their job or wishing they were somewhere else? Are they the negative type that sucks all the energy and enthusiasm from the rest of the team?

Regular personal performance interviews (PPIs) are critical for the success of my business. We tried lots of different ways of holding these. I found the best format was for me to be present with the practice manager. It gives a good balance as we have different styles and we complement each other. We jointly complete the update forms and sign them, agreeing to the action column with due dates. We hold these quarterly. The action columns for all the team get merged into one document that the practice manager finds easy to monitor and update.

A dentist friend of mine used to carry out all the review appraisals of new team members after their induction period. He wanted to make sure they were good enough to join his team. What he did not realise was that because he was in his forties and most of the girls were in their early twenties, he did not have much in common with them. He came across as stern and the girls left the review thinking they were not good enough. Once they got home and spoke to their partners, they came in the next day and handed in their notice. Three promising members of the team left in this manner before he took notice and got another younger colleague to co-interview the girls and help give a more balanced approach.

Brush strokes:

- Ask for referrals
- Understand you can't treat everyone—fire any patient who causes your blood pressure to rise!
- Meet all your referring businesses
- Start lecturing
- Ask in the locality what people know about the local dentist's office
- Get media trained
- Have business cards for your whole team
- Start PPIs

4 It's a journey—what are the signposts?

A journey is best measured in friends rather than miles.
Tim Cahill

So you've worked it out, you know what you want, where you want it and it's full steam ahead. You now need to get on with it, but don't forget to pause for breath every now and then and check you are on the right course.

When I was training for my first triathlon I had to learn how to swim in open water, a very different proposition to swimming when you can see the bottom and you have nice lines in the tiles to show if you are swimming straight or not. You use the least energy head down and swimming freestyle, breathing to the side without lifting your head. The problem is you have no idea where you are going. I was taught to sight. Before you start, you look on the horizon for a large fixed object such as a tree and then aim for that object. Every 30 seconds or so you push down on the water with your leading arm to lift your head and see where you are in relation to that object. You make small corrections to your swimming position as you carry on. Over time you get more accurate and need to look less often. There is no point going full steam ahead and heading off course, then using extra energy to get back on track.

The same is true for life. Are you on track? What is your tree?

It's a journey

How do you know if you are drifting off course? I firmly believe in writing things down. I don't care how great your memory is—if your goals are staring you in the face, ideally every day, you are not going to forget.

So what are you objectives? Be clear and specific. You probably have read about having SMART objectives. They really work. SMART stands for:

Specific, **M**easurable, **A**chievable, **R**ealistic, **T**ime dependent

For example: I want to set up a new two-surgery family-oriented practice in Oxford city centre by July 2012. You can then break this big goal down into individual stages so you can follow your progress, celebrate small successes and not get weighed down by the enormity of the project.

Regular reviews

Just like swimming, you need to check periodically how far you have come and whether you need any mid-course correction. Maybe you are having difficulties getting planning consent and the planning officer has suggested three surgery practices are easier to get consent for.

I am an advocate of getting the whole team involved. You never know where the solution to a problem will come from and life experience comes in all shapes and sizes. I would bring out the existing business plan and see if it is still relevant and what needs to be updated. I have kept all my business plans for Bow Lane. It's fascinating to review them and see what worked and what didn't.

DOS analysis

This is a great way of taking a snapshot of where your business currently is. You start by writing down your current Dangers—what are you concerned about, for example, a new practice opening around the corner, the economy, the backlash against Botox.

Then list the Opportunities available to you NOW. Perhaps a new gym has just opened and there is the chance of a joint venture, or the economic situation favours a push on entry level treatments.

Finally write down your Strengths. What are you strong in? Perhaps you have the only orthodontists for miles around. Are you fully utilising them?

Accountability

Among your team and friends I would shout out what you are aiming for. Not only does it make you accountable to them and less likely to wimp out, it also invites offers of help and support from unlikely places. I remember talking to one of my friends, Elliot Jacobs, about how our team did not have the skills to sell to dentists. However, we did not know the level of demand so were not ready to hire a new salesperson. Elliot knew a part-time freelancer who had a couple of days per week free and we hired him to work on commission. When he followed up all the leads we found that there was not much demand from dentists and that selling direct to dental distributors was the way forward. Having the flexibility of a part-time contractor made a huge difference and made it easier for us to switch direction. It is easy to get caught up in the details, but try to share the headlines only. For example, you could get a member of your team to research digital dental X-ray software.

Remember to be flexible. We spent a lot of time designing our patient lounge. I don't like the term waiting area, it reminds me of hospitals with battle-axe receptionists whose main job seems to be to keep the patient at bay and never let them know when they might actually be seen. An ADA survey found the average waiting time was over seven minutes for a 45 minute appointment. We try to make our lounge feel like a library in a private club. Lots of wood, comfortable sofas and coffee table books.

Not only does it look different, it smells different and sounds different to what you would expect in a dental practice. One of our patient surveys showed that they wanted magazines like *Hello!* It seems whatever their sex or background, people cannot resist the urge to peek at other people's lives, especially celebrities'. A lot of our patients would never dream of buying the magazine but love leafing through it in the lounge.

Keeping an eye on the marketplace

Competition

First and foremost, you should know who your current competitors are. I don't buy into the idea that you have no competition. Everyone has competition. It may not be other dental care professionals—it may be a travel agent. How so? Because they are competing for your patients' hard-earned money.

In Chapter 9 I will be looking at how to differentiate yourself and find your niche. For now, it is important to be aware of any new businesses opening, not just to keep abreast of what is happening in your locality. They will almost certainly have looked at you before opening and they may have spotted something you have overlooked. They may be a business you could partner up with, for example a specialist endodontic practice.

I believe if you are offering something of value and have great relationships with your patients then the only way a new practice can tempt your patients away is by price reductions or offering services that you do not have. If they offer facial aesthetics and you are noticing a demand for that, then either start offering it yourself or develop an alliance with an existing provider so that you can refer patients to each other.

In Chapter 2 I talked about mapping out the existing dental practices and finding out key information such as number of surgeries, what type of dentistry they offer etc. The advice applied to start-ups but I would recommend that you also do this exercise if you have an existing practice.

Trends

Do you know what your patients actually want? Do you know why they come to see you? I asked one of my patients and he said "You always have loads of new cool gadgets like DVD glasses and I can watch a movie during treatment." They have no idea if you are a good dentist or not. All they are interested in is:

- Do you listen to them?
- Did you hurt them?
- Was the treatment comfortable afterwards?
- Does it look good?

Google is the world's leading search engine and you need to know where and when you appear on it. It is three times larger than MSN or Yahoo. Google holds about 10% of the world's information at present and estimates that it will have the entire world's information online within 300 years! There are still dental practices who do not have a website and who don't exist online. You can look at Google Trends to see what people are searching for in your field. For example Invisalign spent millions on an online campaign and their website has over 2.5 million hits per month.

The top global search term related to dentistry is 'dental insurance'.[12] In the US 45 million people have no dental insurance and that is linked to why they don't visit the dentist. Most dental insurance schemes are company purchased rather than individual.

Share with your team/partner

I really believe in informing people close to you what your plans are so that they can help and support you. They need to know how much time the project is likely to take up so they do not feel left out and can plan ahead.

Life partners

John ran a successful shipping business and had a young family. He tried to get home in time for bath time most nights so he could see his kids. An opportunity came up to acquire a rival business and it seemed a perfect fit. He could merge the companies, streamline staff and get some new accounts. He did not want to worry his wife about it as she did not like change and thought they had a perfect life already. But John needed a new challenge. He was getting bored so he just went ahead. It meant at least half the week not getting home for bath time. After a few weeks his wife suspected John was having an affair and started going through his pockets and wallet when she had the opportunity. Of course she found nothing. When the deal was completed John told his wife. She just felt embarrassed and stupid.

For me a great relationship is based on mutual trust and honesty. If John had explained he had a deal going through and would be late home for a few months it would had stopped his wife jumping to the wrong conclusions. Equally she could have asked what was going on.

> **"All problems exist in the absence of a good conversation."**
> *John Niland*

Business partners/team

Of course you need to be careful with how much detail you share and at what time during the project you share things. You need to remember that every person has a different attitude to risk and change. Some of your team just need to know what your are doing currently. Others will like to debate the options, the pros and cons, and reach a team decision. You are the leader and you decide how you disseminate information. For our team meetings I have a blank agenda sheet that is pinned up in the staff room the day after the previous team meeting. The team then have a month to list items they want to discuss. They put their initials by the item so we know who wants to bring it to the team's attention. I then look at all the items with my practice manager and break them down into three categories:

1. Items for discussion. These are things I feel would be best debated out in the open, for example which newspapers we should purchase for the patient lounge.

2. Items for information. This is not up for debate, for example the hours the practice will be open during the holiday season.

3. Items not suitable for discussion at the team meeting, for example something that involves only one or two members, or items that would be better dealt with during the quarterly clinical meetings.

Meetings, meetings and more meetings

Daily

Morning huddles. Every morning, five minutes before the clinical day starts, all the team working that day meet in one of clinical rooms. It is an opportunity to address:

- Patients with outstanding treatments and balances to pay
- Patients who are overdue recall appointments—perhaps they are booked with the hygienist but are overdue a dentist appointment
- Patients who are having sedation or nitrous oxide
- Laboratory work needing to be back
- Other visitors to the practice, for example engineers servicing equipment

I'VE CALLED THIS MEETING TO DISCUSS ABSENTEEISM

The most important habit to get into is to keep the meeting SHORT and SNAPPY to keep everyone's interest. Also the WHOLE TEAM needs to attend. Morning huddles are a great way to take the pulse of the practice.

Weekly

Reception team meeting. To address any issues—30 minutes.

Nurses meeting. Snapshot of stock control and clinical issues—30 minutes.

Management meeting. Over the phone to discuss any problems that have come up in the past week and to check that we are on course with our various targets—15 minutes.

Monthly

Team meeting. At the start of the day; we provide breakfast. We have tried various times but mornings seem to work best—90 minutes.

Web team. Nowadays your internet presence is of critical importance. I receive a monthly report from my website designer and my SEO (search engine optimisation) guy to see what has been going on in the past month, looking at numbers of hits, what pages are most popular, where they find our site from and what's new in the world of websites. If you are running a Google AdWords campaign you need to review this and tweak the keywords, the bids and the maximum daily budget. Once I have the two reports, a quick phone call is usually all that is required to manage these.

Quarterly

Clinical meeting. At the end of the day with all dentists and hygienists—120 minutes followed by dinner, paid for by the practice.

Management meeting. To review the key performance indicators and set targets—60 minutes.

The key performance indicators I look at are:

- Number of new patients
- Referral sources
- Total gross figures, then divided by provider, comparing three months at a time
- Percentage room utilisation—especially useful for multi-surgery practices
- Hourly rate
- Recall rate
- Patient debt

We will come to discuss these in more detail in Chapter 9.

PPIs. We discussed these in Chapter 3—60 minutes.

Annually

Strategic planning days. We take a day off, away from the practice, and hire an outside facilitator. Over the years we have tried many companies and at present Chris Barrow fits well with us (www.coachbarrow.com). He helps run the day and makes sure we get the maximum benefit from everyone's time.

Fun days. We go to a spa and spend the morning over breakfast reviewing the year—what went well, what did not go so well and what we can do better. This tends to be a brainstorming session where everyone has a chance to have a say in what the coming year will be like. We then have lunch together and spend the rest of the day having spa treatments and catching up.

This list obviously does not include Christmas parties and so on but it gives you an idea of the different groups and how often I meet with them. Bow Lane is a limited company with one shareholder (me). If you have a partnership you need to allow time for partnership meetings. There are also meetings with your graphic designer, IT supplier, bank manager and accountants.

Over the years one additional strategy that I have found really works is to randomly take (about once a year) one member of your team out for coffee during the day when you both have a quiet moment. I start the conversation with "How's it going?" and then shut up. In an informal environment away from the office, issues come up that normally would stay buried and cause irritation. They can often be swiftly dealt with.

I believe in the Japanese philosophy of Kaizen—continuous incremental improvement over time. You may have thought you can keep things going just as they are, but in reality unless you are going forwards, even with minute improvements, actually you are going backwards. Which have you decided to do?

Brush strokes:

- Be SMART

- Carry out a DOS analysis

- Map your connections

- Categorise the items on your meeting agenda

- Schedule meetings 12 months in advance

- Hire a facilitator for your strategic planning day

5 Providing what your patients want

Some people want it to happen, some wish it would happen, others make it happen.

Michael Jordan

Perspective

Over the last 20 years the way we work, play and communicate has changed dramatically. The worldwide web was invented by a British engineer, Tim Berners-Lee, in 1990; can you remember a time without it?

Re-live the pain of purchasing a vacuum cleaner before the days of the internet. If you were lucky you read magazine reviews, otherwise you turned up at your local appliance store and asked what they had that matched your budget. Usually they did not have that model in stock and you ended up buying a model over your budget in a putrid colour scheme. It was generally an unpleasant experience.

I had to purchase a vacuum cleaner recently. I was driving in the direction of the shopping centre to get one but hit a traffic jam. While stationary (I don't want points on my driving licence) I used my iPhone to check which model had the best reviews, then see where it was cheapest. The best was Argos. On their site I could check the local store's stock level—just one left but I was able to reserve it. Once the traffic was moving again I drove into the car park, walked to the store, swiped my credit card, entered the order number and two minutes later the vacuum cleaner was there. I walked out of the store and as I was less than five minutes in the car park did not have to pay anything. What a fabulous experience.

In 2001 Apple changed the way we purchase and listen to music forever with the iPod. This is one of the many ways in which our lives are being changed by technology.

Dentistry specifically has been dragged out of the dark ages; it started as we know it in the eighteenth century. Gone are the days that your only option was to pull out a tooth. Now that is the last thing we offer. When it is unavoidable, the whole emphasis is on making the patient comfortable and causing minimal damage to the surrounding tissues.

In the past we thought filling teeth was actually good for them as it prevented cavities! The patients had no choice—they just went to their closest practitioner and put up with the pain. This has led to millions of people with a phobia of dentists. Now with the migrant workforce and the internet, patients are often more informed about treatment options than the practitioner. Patients have a choice, even in the state sector, and they want to be listened to.

Your patients can decide where they receive their dental care. My practice is in London's financial district. A few of my patients also have another dental health care provider. They have grown up with their family dentist and have established a level of trust that is very difficult to break. They find it helpful to have one practice near home and one nearer work. They also can have one practice for their routine maintenance and another one for reconstruction work or aesthetic treatment. I remember once asking one of my patients why he was seeing me for a crown. He said Dr. X was OK for check-ups and hygiene work but he wouldn't trust him to do any treatment because he was too old.

Other Industries

I find I get my best inspiration from other industries. I analyse why I use certain brands, which hotels I like to stay at; I ask myself "When did I last have a 'wow' customer experience?" I try to get to the core of what made it stand out. It usually boils down to people doing something extraordinary.

I used to ride a scooter to work. I thought about the risks and benefits and decided that the freedom it gave me to know the exact journey time and have a more productive day was worth the increased risk of injury. To mitigate the risks I only used it for commuting and always wore the best protective gear money could buy. Considering what I was wearing, I am sure people expected me to jump on a Harley instead of a Vespa! Last year that all changed. I skidded on the bike and landed on the road with a crunch.

Anyone who has ever broken a bone knows the sound and the feeling when you know you have done something serious. I could not bend my elbow so could not move the bike. A passing rider lifted my bike and parked it for me. I was lucky enough to have the accident five minutes walk from a hospital. I was seen in five minutes, had a digital X-ray in 15 minutes and was deciding on treatment options with the nurse practitioner within 45 minutes. The NHS in the UK is amazing for emergency care, especially at 7am on a Friday. Not a drunk in sight!

I walked out of the hospital wearing a sling, having being told "No work for six weeks and no yoga for 12 weeks." It seems strange now, but I was staring at people with two good arms and felt jealous of them. Not surprisingly, that was everyone! Then I thought "I am lucky to walk away with just a broken elbow and it would be good for me to slow down and find alternative exercises." The next day it was not as bad as I expected and I could move the arm a bit. I strongly believe whatever you put your mind to you can achieve. Three days later I was in the Bikram studio, and you know what—it was the first time the arm did not ache. Even though I could only do 14 of the 26 postures, I felt I had already proved the doctors wrong. I was back at work treating patients in five days, though no extractions for two weeks.

Recovery was very speedy and at the six-week review the doctor said to me "The reason you healed so quickly is you actually ENJOY your job and sport and want to get better. Most of my patients use their injuries as an excuse not to achieve."

You get what you wish for.

Why do you think a motorbike is one of the most dangerous methods of transport and a passenger jet one of the safest? Checklists! In aviation they were devised in 1935. Boeing unveiled its latest model, the 299, which could carry five times as many bombs as its competition. On the day of the test flight just after lift-off the plane crashed, killing two of the five crew including the pilot. The cause of the crash was pilot error. The newspapers said it was too much airplane for one man to fly. They could not imagine a more experienced pilot and crew, so what would Boeing do? They created checklists as there were too many procedures for one person to remember. Four checklists were developed—take-off, flight, before landing, and taxi-ing. This simple list led to 1.8 million miles flown in the 299 without one single incident.

The tragedy had exposed the fallibility of human memory, especially in so-called routine matters. This approach has been carried over into medicine, initially with checks for nursing staff for the five vital signs: temperature, pulse, blood pressure, respiratory rate and pain. Doctors rebelled initially, saying that was stuff for nurses. In 2001 a doctor from Johns Hopkins

Hospital, Peter Pronovost, introduced an intensive care checklist protocol that during an 18-month period saved 1,500 lives and $100 million in the United States alone.

With increasing legislation isn't it time checklists were brought into dental practice? We use a checklist to ensure instruments are correctly sterilised but perhaps as we are now more focused on patient outcomes and clinical governance they should be routinely in place for all kinds of treatment. If it's good enough for pilots...

What do patients want?

Do you know what your patients are interested in, what they are looking for in a dental relationship, and why they chose you in particular to deliver it? If not, don't you think that should be something you found out about? In chapter 8 I will talk more about this but for now, we all know that you do not need teeth simply in order to eat. What does a healthy attractive smile say about you? It says you take care of yourself and you are happy.

A recent survey by Dr. Anne Beall suggested a new smile will make you appear more intelligent, interesting, successful and wealthy.[13] The survey used four pictures of patients before they had cosmetic dentistry and four of the same patients after they had completed treatment. The respondents did not know they were looking at dental patients and had to make a snap judgement on the people in the pictures.

Why do your patients actually come to see you? A quarter of people only visit the dentist when they have trouble with their teeth, according to the UK's adult dental health survey.[14] Attendance globally at the dentist is at its lowest since 2001.

What drives people to visit the dentist, and how can you motivate them to attend? In 2004 the American Academy of Cosmetic Dentistry asked people what they wanted to improve about their smile. The most common response was "whiter and brighter teeth". Toothpaste manufacturers know this. They suggest their toothpaste will make your teeth whiter, but they go further. They suggest you will be more confident and attractive, thus appealing to the love instinct. You will belong to the group with an attractive smile.

According to BDTA Spotlight 2009, 78% of adults' last appointment was for routine dentistry. The survey showed that 41% of people did not go because of cost.

How to find out

I believe in surveying patients. I regularly ask my patients what they think of the Bow Lane experience and encourage them to reply by explaining why their opinions matter and how giving their views can benefit others. For example:

> We at Bow Lane Dental Group hope you are enjoying having healthy confident smiles.
>
> However, in order to deliver even better quality service to you, we would love your thoughts. Knowing what you think of the service is vital to us, as this helps us to learn, in order to continuously improve.
>
> To show our appreciation, for every completed survey we will make a DONATION to Facing the World, a children's charity that helps disadvantaged children recover from facial deformities.
>
> Thank you.
>
> James

We donate money to charity for every completed survey and we get on average a 10% response rate. Over time I have devised a way to get the highest number of responses:

1. The form should take less than two minutes to complete

2. An online form with just one click to join works best

3. Make it anonymous, but give the respondent the option of putting their name

4. Give respondents an incentive to complete it by a certain time, e.g. supporting a donation to charity

5. Subject line—make it intriguing

6. Send it out at the right time. We found that Tuesday at 11am is the time when the email is most likely to be opened. Research shows Monday is a bad time as people are looking to clear their inbox as quickly as possible and may be recovering from a heavy weekend. On Fridays they are wrapping up their work in preparation for the weekend. Try to avoid sending out survey appeals around holiday time. As a general rule, either 11am or 1pm on Tuesday, Wednesday or Thursday are the best times to deliver an email.

I use Survey Monkey (www.surveymonkey.com) as it is clean, quick and simple to use and has great tools to analyse the results. They have a free version with limited capability or a full service product for a small monthly fee.

Another way of surveying our patients is more successful but also more time-consuming. We get the entire team to help identify our top 25 patients. They are our raving fans: they refer the most number of new patients and love spending time with us —and us with them. We call them personally and explain that we value their feedback as they are our top patients, then carry out the survey over the phone. At the end we send them a small gift to show our appreciation.

Once you have found out what your patients want, you need to filter the results with your brand. Just because something has come up in a survey you do not necessarily want to immediately put it in place. For example, if some patients ask you to deliver facial aesthetics and Botox, you may decide that this does not fit the profile of a family-oriented practice. The survey showed that there is patient demand. It may be that you get an independent practitioner to offer facial aesthetic services at your clinic or set up a referral service for interested patients to see a local expert.

Our surveys often pick up areas where we may have not achieved perfect customer service. This gives us a chance to rectify the problem. We are all human and make mistakes—it is how you deal with those mistakes which sets you apart. For example, one patient mentioned in the survey that he was still waiting for the treatment plan he was promised two weeks ago. We immediately retrieved the plan and sent it by courier with a note. He booked in the same day.

You comply—shout about it!

Are you at the forefront of technology? Do you exceed cross-infection protocols? Why not shout about it. I know when I was looking at surgeons and private hospitals to have a wrist operated on, I looked for membership of the right organisations, an up-to-date website, certification and evidence of good cleanliness of staff and facilities. Why would your patients not do the same? One of the most overlooked areas is the toilets. If you can't keep them spotless and well stocked, then what hope is there for the operating rooms? That's what your patients think. If you meet BDA Good Practice Scheme or Denplan Excel standards, say so on your website and in your literature, and make sure all the team know what it takes to get those acknowledgments when patients ask about them.

It takes a lot of effort and a large financial investment to comply, so let all your patients know about it. Your patients will often also be in businesses that have a lot of red tape and compliance procedures, so they will appreciate the work it takes to stay up to date.

If your particular regulations require you to be inspected, then what a great opportunity to send a press release to your local paper saying your practice was recently inspected and met and exceeded all the latest guidelines. Regulatory bodies are increasingly publishing their findings on their website for the public to peruse and use as criteria for choosing a dental practice.

One of my good friends, Daniel Priestley, talks about the seven hour rule. On average it takes someone seven hours before making a big decision. Many new patients will have invested a lot of time looking at various dental websites, watching videos of procedures and the dental professionals on YouTube before deciding who has the level of trust, understanding and rapport they want. I often see new patients who act as if this is not their first meeting with me. They feel they know me and understand my treatment philosophy before I have even sat them in the dental chair. They know a lot about the dental procedure they think they need. They are not always correct but they are increasingly well informed. It is also a great screening process as the people who are not interested in your philosophy or services don't even bother to pick up the phone. Now we are seeing many more serious patients who want to invest time and money in their oral health care.

Increasing legislation

In the UK we have a regulatory body called the Care Quality Commission and for the first time they are in charge of regulating dental practices. They have produced a ream of guidelines, all concerned with patient outcomes. They don't care how you get there but they do want consistent, predictable, evidence-based results. It all sounds great but it has been rushed through without proper consultation and dentists are finding that many checks are being unnecessarily duplicated. For example, we all have to get enhanced criminal record checks when we have had these already. Some dentists are digging their heels in and refusing to register and risk being prosecuted for practising illegally. Some contributors to dental forums are calling for people to take to the streets and stage protest rallies. Can you imagine much public sympathy for a group of dentists complaining about red tape!

The proliferation of bureaucracy and regulatory bodies seems to be a global phenomenon. The great benefit is that it weeds out the underperformers and encourages practitioners close to retirement to call it a day before another inspector visits them. The average age for a dentist to retire is 65, which is currently when the UK state pension kicks in.

Working with insurance companies

My colleagues in America tell me there is a battle going on with insurance providers. Some patients take out dental insurance and expect everything to be covered, and only accept those dentists and treatment plans that are covered by their particular provider. I feel it is a slippery slope. Once you start pandering to external companies and changing your business model, you start to lose control of your vision. By all means offer insurance, but take some time to stop and think about who you want to work for. I know we all work for the government. Every year the 'tax freedom' day—the day we actually start working for ourselves—gets later and later. In the UK this has for the first time crept into June.

My philosophy is that we work with our patients to provide them with the best possible clinical care, using the best materials. My reception team then work with the patient's insurance provider to maximise their reimbursement. Our role is to complete the paperwork and take away the hassle of haggling with the insurance companies. WE drive the clinical treatment, not the insurance company.

With this in mind, and realising there was no perfect cover for my patients, I worked with DPAS to produce the Smile for Life™ Membership Scheme. It offers:

- Two visits to the hygienist per year
- One recall examination with the dentist
- All clinically required X-rays
- 10% off all other treatments (except specialist services)
- Worldwide dental insurance against accident

- PLUS free tooth whitening. This uses a home whitening system. We worked out that as we make the bleaching trays in-house it actually cost us only about $30 (less than £20) for a complete home whitening kit.

Patients pay £19.99 per month and are then tied in via direct debit to our practice. This allows them to budget for their dental care; the bonus for us is that they tend to be more loyal and much less likely to visit another dentist.

Think about your practice—some patients find paying $100 or £60 a time for a hygiene visit a bit much. Paying a small amount regularly by direct debit is much easier to swallow.

📖 Recommended reading: Atul Gawande, The Checklist Manifesto

Brush strokes:

- Think about your last 'wow' experience—can you replicate it?

- What routine procedure could benefit from a checklist?

- Survey your patients

- Identify and call your top 25 patients

- What recent legislation did you have to comply with? Have you shouted about it?

- Help your patients to complete insurance forms, but remember who you work for

6 Use the global market to your advantage

The Difficult is that which can be done immediately; the Impossible that which takes a little longer.
George Santayana

The world is your oyster, but how many of us actually believe that and harness the power of global marketing? I remember the first time it hit home was a few years ago. I was approaching the last few days of a two-week holiday and images started to appear of all the jobs I had to do when I returned home. An empty fridge and having to do the shopping ready for a dinner party the next day. Then I thought "Let's log on to my Tesco (Peapod) account and reorder my previous order." Five minutes later I knew that one hour after I arrived home my groceries would also be arriving.

I want to take you to a global 24/7 mindset where anything is possible at any time—you just need to think creatively. The world is getting more connected and faster. Things that used to take multiple visits now can be completed in one go. You want a custom-made all-ceramic crown in an hour? No problem with CEREC. You want straight teeth in eight weeks? No problem with the Inman Aligner.

From a beach in the Caribbean you can be having a virtual tour around a dental practice in Los Angeles and make an online appointment for a consultation.

What is currently bugging you at work? Think about other industries that have a similar problem: how did they solve it? Take low-cost airlines—as the seats get booked the price goes up. How about rewarding your patients who see the hygienist regularly and give them a lower rate if they pre-book and pre-pay their three-monthly recare appointments.

Level playing field

It's great that small companies can look as big as large corporations—sometimes bigger. The internet has flattened the world. The website for your single operatory practice can look as impressive as that of a global corporate with 120 locations. Often we have an advantage in healthcare, especially dental care, as ours is very much a relationship business. As a smaller business we have the opportunity to really get to know our patients and show our true personalities and differences. This should come across in all your patient interactions, what big corporates call customer touch points. Each opportunity to 'touch' or interact with a patient is your chance to convert a patient to a fan who will tell their friends and cascade your marketing message by word of mouth.

Small businesses can be more in tune with current trends and what their patients want. Even more importantly, they can change instantly and implement new strategies the very next day. They do not have a board of directors to answer to and a committee to approve any changes.

The population is more mobile today, fewer people end up living and working in the town they were born in. In the book *The Economics of Earnings*, Solomon W. Polachek and W. Stanley Siebert say the average person now has just over eight jobs in their lifetime. Think about your parents—they often stuck with one or two at most. People are more demanding now than they ever were, thanks to the ease of often free global communication. It's not just about keeping up with the Joneses next door; today it's the Husseins in the next country and the Chans in the next continent. We are also seeing the growing phenomenon of dental tourism, where patients actively seek treatment in other countries due to the cost or lack of availability in their home town.

Patients seeking treatment elsewhere

There seem to be three reasons why patients look to other dental clinics:

a) **New treatments and approaches.** With the transparency provided by the internet, patients can see the range of treatments you offer and the ethos of your practice. Do you offer minimal invasive dentistry with a team approach, or perhaps you are a family-centred practice? They may be missing a tooth and their current dentist does not offer dental implants, so they are looking for a clinic that specialises in implants. Nowadays they can find so much information online that could probably place their own implant if they could get hold of the equipment. Obviously without six years dental training their first one would be a horrible failure but perhaps after the fifteenth one they may not do a bad job!

When we started to offer minimal invasive veneers we had a massive increase in new patient enquiries, often from patients of very well established clinics. They liked the fact that there was an option to improve their smiles without drilling away healthy enamel and without injections. One patient actually came from a dentist who offered this treatment but didn't make his patients aware of it. Our external marketing was more obvious to this patient than his internal marketing (non-existent).

b) **Price.** Some people will be shopping on price alone, and on the basis of transparency I believe you should be proud of your fees. As a consumer I am always a bit wary of companies that have no prices on their website. I feel they have something to hide. You do not need to have every option on your website but you should at least state the most popular treatments and offer a guide price for other treatments, say crowns from $1,000 or £600. Others will be looking at your expertise, patient stories (testimonials), location, opening hours, insurance coverage, languages spoken etc. With all new patients it is very important to capture the data not only on how they found out about your clinic but also what attracted them to book an appointment with you rather than someone else, as there is always an alternative. A new patient was telling me in great detail how great her previous dentist was and how much she liked the rest of the team and his hygienist. I asked what brought her to our clinic and she said she felt like the dentist was always trying to sell her something. Eventually that was why she left.

When will there be price comparison websites for dental practices? It is only a matter of time. Will you be seduced by the price-sensitive customer or will you stand firm?

Price is what has led to the massive increase in tooth whitening outside the normal dental environment. In shopping centres and high streets around the country you see tooth whitening being offered by non-dental trained 'technicians'. Often they are beauticians who have been on a half-day training course and are being told by their managers that whitening teeth is safe and easy and that dentists are just ripping off the public with exorbitant prices. I still cannot understand how you can whiten someone's teeth without diagnosing the cause of the discolouration and assessing the health of their teeth first. They are also attracting the kind of patients who don't go to the dentist because they are scared of dentistry and are worried that the dentist will tell them off or find other treatment that needs doing. That is a failure on part of the dental profession and should be something we start to rectify. We should be making dentistry available to everyone by:

1. Transparent pricing with multiple payment options

2. Offering a less clinical environment—clean but not sterile looking

3. Open communication without fear of blame or judge-ment—no blame dentistry

4. Making it easy—easy to book, no jargon, talk to them on their level, focus on outcomes

c) **Breakdown in communication.** This is increasingly common. The patient does not feel listened to, or some of your treatment has failed. In the case of failed treatment, the dentist is often not even aware that a problem exists. You assume that as the patient has not returned the treatment must have been a success. With some people it is less embarrassing to find a new dentist than to confront their current dentist about the failure (it could be an aesthetic failure, broken filling or chronic pain).

Professionals seeking training/equipment from alternate markets

I remember my first professional purchase abroad, a MacBook that was 17.5% cheaper than in the UK. You get a certain satisfaction from being smart and saving money. That is exactly how your patients feel. They don't know the difference between your all-ceramic Lava crown made by a top ceramist who segmentally layers the porcelain and cuts back to produce a lifelike restoration and a cap. Once they are a patient of yours you can educate them. I remember a patient who was very price conscious and we had to do a crown for her. One month later part of the crown fractured (I am happy to share my failures globally). She came in and after I had apologised I remade the crown. She came back and said that was why she was happy to pay extra: we had pride in our work and would go to any lengths to make it right, without question. People are happy to pay extra for peace of mind; you just need to give them great customer service.

These are some of the reasons that people seek other markets:

a) Currency fluctuations. It may just be cheaper in another country, as with the MacBook.

b) That's where the product is or where the equipment is sold. I looked into different composite resin courses which where not tied to a specific manufacturer. I started to look globally and found that Newton Fahl's course in Brazil fitted what I was looking for, so I booked it (www.fahl.com. br). There may be demand for a certain type of dentist in a specific market or that just may be where the founder of the course practises.

Certain pieces of equipment may not have a distributor in your country so you have no choice but to buy it abroad.

Just be wary of the customs and import duty which can add as much as 25% to the price. It is often less on used equipment, or it may pay you to travel to the country and collect it in person if it is not too big to fit in your luggage.

c) You can combine your purchase with a holiday. A few years ago dental skiing holidays were all the rage. You could put the trip down to Continuing Professional Development and write it off against tax, whether you actually attended the CPD course or not. The focus has changed now; the course content has to be excellent, along with the provider—and can they deliver it! I am noticing more and more international courses that offer a once-in-a-lifetime experience at the same time. The providers realise that people have lots of things trying to grab their attention and their money. Time is precious and if you can get outstanding global learning along with an experience you will never forget, it becomes a Must Do. How cool is swimming with Caribbean manatees in a break session? People learn best when they are excited and perhaps a bit apprehensive.

Seek the best team members

Have you thought about what qualities you are looking for in a new team member? Is it just someone who turns up and does the job? The number one attribute I look for in a new recruit is ATTITUDE. You cannot train attitude, it is something that is inherently in them, nurtured from childhood. Over the years I have found that people from Australia and New Zealand almost always have a fabulous work ethic. They want to do their best and put in 100%. The skills we can teach; we can train clinical skills, communication and leadership but they have to want to learn.

So how about you, what are the non-negotiable attributes for your new team member? Not only do you need a job description, I find a personality description also helps. You can use your existing team as a guide; if you are setting up a new team, think about the best team member you had the pleasure of working alongside in the past. What were their qualities?

Great—now you have got your template for the ideal candidate. How do you find them?

a) Tell your team that you are looking and ask if they know someone suitable.

b) Tell your patients you are expanding and looking for someone new.

c) Check your store of enquiries and CVs from previous applicants. I am privileged to receive applications every week from people who would like to be part of Bow Lane. I acknowledge every one and the interesting ones I file for the future. When the time comes for a new team member I filter through the applications I have had for that specific role and contact the good ones to see if they are still looking. I remember I recently hired a female dentist,

Sandra. She had sent me her CV five months previously as we had a mutual friend who was helping Sandra to make her CV more attractive to future employers. I met Sandra and tweaked her CV and thought nothing of it. When we expanded and a position came available I remembered her, brought her in for interview and now she works at Bow Lane.

d) Network dental events. Ask your colleagues, you may find great people looking for new positions. Incidentally, articles suggest that dentists who are members of dental organisations have a lower suicide rate than those who are not.[15]

JANE WOKE UP WITH THIRTY NEW FACEBOOK FRIENDS...
...AND NO IDEA HOW THEY GOT THERE

e) Use social media like Facebook and LinkedIn. My last dental nurse from Australia found our practice via Facebook and sent me a message and CV. Two months later she came to the UK and now works for us. Well over half (59%) of the dental professionals surveyed in UK stated that they use social networking sites[16] and most of them logged in daily.

f) Global dental online communities—Dentaltown, AACD, BACD websites.

g) Gumtree/Craigslist.

It was in 1879 that the *New York Times* first talked about the Law of Attraction—tell the universe you are looking and it will come to you. I am sure you have never noticed all the people who cycle to work until one day you decide it would be good for you to cycle to work. You suddenly notice the plethora of cycles.

Brush strokes:

- When you have a new treatment or service make sure you inform your patients via e-newsletters, brochures and talking to them

- Make it easy for patients—booking, price list, less jargon, no blame dentistry, focus on outcomes

- Hire for attitude

- Draft a personality description for members of your team

- Look globally for your equipment and training

- Use social media to help find and screen new team members

7 Build a team you can be proud of

I've always found that the speed of the boss is the speed of the team.
Lee Iacocca

As Michael Gerber says, a dental practice relies on a great dentist and a dental business relies on a team with great systems. When things don't go to plan it is usually because of a breakdown in the system. So you review the system, modify it and try again. Once the systems work the business has less reliance on individuals and becomes more consistent. In the last chapter we talked about how to attract the right people to your business. Let's now talk about getting the right people in the right jobs, growing and nurturing them.

You can't be good at everything

So what are you good at? You need a baseline to work from. One exercise that can be hard at first is to take a look at your strengths and weaknesses. Take some time now to write them down:

Strengths   Weaknesses

. . . .

. . . .

. . . .

. . . .

. . . .

. . . .

You can also work with a personal coach or ask close friends to help. I have worked with various coaches over the years. One of the greatest advantages of a good coach is that they have no hidden agendas and give feedback based on facts, not emotions. They won't tell you what they think you want to hear. There is no sugar coating. Once I have my list I then look at ways I can grow my strengths and delegate my weaknesses.

There are various standardised ways of measuring knowledge, abilities, attitudes and personality traits. These so-called psycho-metric tests are used to help select the best applicants for a job. Say you have a practice manager position available. You can test any current team members who are interested in the position to see if they have the right traits for that position. These tests are used by multinational companies, but often they look just at the negatives. I have more respect for Kolbe tests (www.kolbe.com) as they focus on natural abilities and talents and help you to develop them.

So now you know what you're not great at, or just don't like doing. Start addressing your weaknesses by outsourcing them or attracting team members who are strong in those areas. It always astounds me how some people seem to surround themselves with individuals who have the same talents and then wonder why nothing gets done!

I am a firm believer in cross training. This allows everyone to have more variety in their work and you can move resources around as and when they are needed. Take one of the simplest tasks, making bleaching trays. All our team can make them, including the practice manager. They all know how to pour and trim the models and make the trays. This does not mean no-one has responsibility for a task; it just gives us flexibility when someone is sick, on holiday or just busy on something else. We know we will have someone who can step into their shoes until they are free again.

You shouldn't do it all yourself

Have you noticed how some dentists always seem stressed? They take ownership of their patients' problems, have mood swings and bring domestic issues into the surgery. If they have a difficult fit appointment they don't sleep well the night before. I believe that your home and work happiness are inextricably connected. Some people are good at switching off from issues at home, but eventually these will come to the surface. Take a good look at your home situation. Is there something that you are tolerating or avoiding taking action on?

How do you eat an elephant? One bite at a time!

I remember a married dentist who was having an affair, but at work he pretended nothing was going on. Over time he got more cocky and less discreet; members of the team overheard parts of telephone conversations and pieced it all together. He started to take mobile calls during treatment and it began to affect his work. The nurses did not feel it was their place to comment. They told me about the calls, but not the nature of them. Before I could speak to him, his wife found out. Now they are getting a divorce.

Life is all about balance. If you are happy and content in your home life it is likely that will manifest itself in your work life. We spend a large part of our lives in the workplace. Why work somewhere that you are not content, valued and respected?

As we all know, dentists are control freaks. But micro-managing is a recipe for failure, leading to disconnected team relationships and high staff turnover. People undertake tasks in different ways. Once you get to know your people you can tailor your instructions in a way that connects best with them. I find one of the best ways is in a simple email. I outline the task, the timeframe, any additional resources they may need, and who to report back to.

Your role is?

Dentists tend to be Type A personalities with controlling natures. I should know! I want you to step back and answer this question: what is the unique ability that only you bring to the table? Some may say "just dentistry"; others "fix the computers when they freeze!" Take some time to write down your core strengths. You may have some others that are not core but which you love doing; for example I love working with our graphic designers to develop simple effective images.

Core strengths

. . . .

. . . .

. . . .

The best leaders concentrate hard on their core strengths. When I ask audiences to name the best-known business people the most common answers in the UK are Richard Branson, Lakshmi Mittal and Steve Jobs. In the US they are Donald Trump, Bill Gates and Warren Buffett. But few of us have ever actually met these people, so it's hard to directly learn from them. I prefer people who are in my circle of friends, people I wouldn't think twice about calling up on the phone. You can learn much more from these people. Do they focus on their core strengths? You may have put them on a pedestal, because they don't do it all themselves. If they are great it will look effortless, but ask them about the back office team who make them look so good. Later we will talk about recruiting and retaining your own support team.

What are you core strengths?

Everything involved in running a dental practice that does not use your core strengths you should DELEGATE. I know dentists are rubbish at delegating but your hourly rate is high, so answering patients' emails and writing treatment plans is not the best use of your time. Train another member of your team to do that, and get on with what you are great at.

Creating and maintaining a successful business requires a lot of different skills. Gerber describes three types of business people:

1. Those who work in the business, the technicians. This definition includes other dentists who work for you because essentially they have a tactical role. Without dentists there is no business. You may fulfil this role much of the time but when you do, basically you are working for a salary.

2. The managers. They invent and develop the systems through which your vision is realised. The manager's work is both strategic and tactical. The manager focuses on the present and using the team to achieve results. They are the planners and organisers.

3. The entrepreneur. The entrepreneur's work is strategic in nature; it involves focusing on the future and developing a vision of where they can take their business. This vision is specific in terms of how the practice serves the wants and needs of the owner.

Roy Ash said a classic entrepreneur bites off more than he or she can chew, hoping to learn how to swallow.

What's the difference between strategy and tactics?

Being simplistic, strategy refers to the 'what' and the 'why', tactics refers to the 'how'. Strategic thinking, planning and actions require the ability to look at the big picture, recognise patterns and trends, establish priorities, anticipate and have alternatives available as necessary. Strategic plans are driven by the vision, the mission and the goals of the business. I am always concerned about producing mission statements as once they are done no-one ever bothers to look at them again.

On the other hand, tactical is the 'doing it' part of the business, ensuring that the strategic goals are met. Tactics are essentially the detailed actions needed to achieve those goals. Both are inter-dependent as tactical activity (in the right area) is what makes the strategies work.

What sort of practice do you want to run? Most dental practices are dominated by technicians, to the detriment of the overall business.

What matters most is the vision. Consider the case of Ray Kroc, the man behind McDonald's. He had a passion for food and was a good technician and manager. But he was a great visionary. He realised that while his customers bought his hamburgers, what they were really buying into was the name. His customers got a consistent experience every time they turned up at his restaurants. Burgers may have been what they bought, but what he was selling was McDonald's.

Kroc also talked about turnkey operations, processes which anyone who had read the manual could run. No matter who purchased a McDonald's franchise, it worked because it was a system-based model.

It is critical that someone is the leader of the organisation. They need to lead by example. My favourite quote about leadership is "someone who inspires others to become leaders" and I feel that I have achieved something when I see people I have taught take on leadership roles themselves.

Motivating and retaining your team

The average dental practice has seven employees.[10] How are you going to keep them engaged? One of the biggest fallacies about work is that people do it just for the money. There has been a lot of research in this area and a **sense of achievement** and **having that achievement recognised** appear to be the two strongest motivators. Positive working relationships also appear key, with quotes such as "having trust and respect from colleagues" and "being supported by those around you" indicating that social support is a significant motivator. Look at the 'Like' function on Facebook—what purpose does it have apart from making people feel good about their network? One of the biggest things that made people feel bad at work was when colleagues undermined them. That was complained about even more than working with difficult or unpleasant people.

So how do you know if they are happy? Team turnover or absenteeism are reliable indicators of dissatisfaction and also have a knock-on effect on productivity. A poorly motivated team is not productive. Draw up a list of all your team members, then list the number of days absent per person. That is one indicator of an unhappy team member. It is unreliable to take this in isolation—other factors need to taken into account such as a chronic illness—but it is a warning sign. I pay my team bonuses and one of the criteria is days absent, so they know that any missed days will affect them financially. We try to be fair—our staff are cross trained, so if a member of the reception team is not well enough for front desk duties they may be happy to do back office tasks such as recalls or answering email enquiries.

Appraisals and feedback are important motivational mechanisms. We talked earlier about PPIs so if this is a subject close to your heart, take another look at Chapter 3.

Fun stuff

People who play together tend to be more relaxed in one another's company and gel better as a team. We are all equal on an away day and the idea is just to have fun. We have done lots of different activities; most of the suggestions come from the team or patients who have mentioned cool things they have done at work. These include:

- Bowling
- Cooking lessons
- Spa sessions
- Paintballing
- Premier film trip
- Television recording studio
- Comedy club
- Houses of Parliament tour
- Go-karting

Money

We have to talk about it. I believe in paying the going rate. I usually speak to recruitment firms to get the average for a particular job or locality. I want to attract team members who know they get paid well for their effort, but want to work with us because they believe in the ethos of the practice and the type of dentistry we offer. We will help and nurture them along their career and they will get opportunities that other practices do not offer them.

Continuing Professional Development (CPD)

We enrol and pay for any CPD that team members think will further their training and improve their skills. All we ask is that they produce a summary for us afterwards and then present the key learnings at the next staff meeting to share with the team.

Bonuses

The majority of practices offer staff bonuses. If you speak to ten management gurus you will get ten different notions of what makes a good bonus scheme. I've tried them all and they all work to some extent. Some are horribly complicated. We decided to keep it simple:

Unless we make a profit, there will be NO bonus. I then take 5% of the profit figure (an arbitrary number but it works) and that goes into that month's bonus pot. I then look at each team member's attendance record for the month. 100% attendance gets 100% bonus and pro rata. I then work out each person's salary as a percentage of the total salary bill. So if the practice manager has 18% of the salary bill and she had 100% attendance, she gets 18% of the bonus pot. Any money left over (only if someone did not have 100% attendance) is carried forward to the next month's pot.

Staff bonus calculator			
Month			January
Net profit			$51,015.10
Bonus percentage	5.00%		$2550.76
	Salary	Percentage of total	
PM	$32,750.00	18.69%	$476.64
Head nurse	$23,500.00	13.41%	$342.02
Receptionist	$23,308.00	13.30%	$339.22
Nurse	$23,000.00	13.12%	$334.74
Nurse	$22,500.00	12.84%	$327.46
Receptionist	$26,205.00	14.95%	$381.38
Nurse	$24,000.00	13.69%	$349.29
Total	$175,263.00	100.00%	$2,550.76
Total profit for year	$310,816.10		
Total bonus for year	$8,935.15		

If this sounds like something you could use in your practice, send me a request at jamesgoolnik.com and I will send you a simple Excel bonus calculator. Once you have it set up you only need to enter the bonus pot figure and deduct for any missed days.

Remember, a successful team is not just about attracting the right members. It's more important to retain them, the same as with your patients. A dentist in London with a fabulous practice was hiring every two months. I thought she was expanding rapidly and needed a larger team but later it came to light that each member only managed to last two months. She went though all the expense of hiring, paying introduction fees and putting the new member through an expensive and time-consuming induction, only for them to leave. What was going wrong? It was this dentist; she was very controlling and bossy. The new members of the team would get scared and resign. The existing team had got used to her, realising that her bark was worse than her bite. Eventually they put a business manager in place as a buffer between the dentist and the rest of the team and persuaded her to release control of team selection and induction. The next recruit stayed and was still there 12 months later!

Everyone's on a different journey

As we talked about earlier, you have your journey mapped out (you should by now) and it will change over time. Your team members also have their own individual journeys. They may want to find a partner, settle down and have kids. They may want to breed dogs in the country. It's not personal if they leave your team—it's just that your journey and theirs have moved in different directions. As part of your PPI appraisal and looking at training needs in the future, you should have a good idea of what that journey may look like professionally.

There is no point holding someone back who is excellent at what they currently do but wants to do something else, as they will eventually leave to pursue it. So why not actively help and encourage them? They will be a lot happier at work if you do so. This is especially common when they go off to get married and have kids. Often they come back and work part-time once the kids are old enough.

One way I encourage my team to think about their future is by getting them to complete a painted picture, like we talked about in Chapter 2. This is when they imagine where they will be in three years from now and how they see their life, in every aspect. Get them to write this down and if they want to share the professional part with you so that you can help that dream happen quicker, then great!

📖 Recommended reading: <u>Michael Gerber</u>, The E-Myth Physician

Brush strokes:

- Take the Kolbe test

- Hire and delegate to cover your weaknesses

- Look to your friends for your role models

- Decide what type of business you want to run

- Think strategically

- Look at your absenteeism records—are your team trying to tell you something?

- What fun event are you going to organise for your team?

- Put a simple bonus scheme in place

8 You need to be one step ahead of your patient

Your most unhappy customers are your greatest source of learning.
Bill Gates

I firmly believe that in all aspects of your life you are either growing or shrinking. There is no such thing as standing still. The market is constantly changing and what works well for you now may not work in three months time. Consumers are more aware than ever and are looking to be taken care of and offered the best value for their money. They want to be treated by a forward-thinking, proactive dental practice rather than a reactionary one.

The best scenario is where you are continually educating your patients about what is new and how it impacts on their dental care and their lives, whether it the latest text message reminder service or aromatherapy oil to calm and relax them. The second-best scenario is where they come in clutching the latest celebrity magazine and ask you about the wrinkle-lifting veneers that Hilary Duff just had fitted. You then educate the patient about the procedure. The worst scenario is they ask you and you don't know anything about it so they go to someone else!

Consumer awareness

Never before have our patients had more accurate information available to them at the click of a button. It may not be relevant to their clinical case but it is still accurate and it is our responsibility to guide them in the treatment planning stage.

The power of publicity cannot be overstated. We were invited onto a breakfast TV show to demonstrate two different tooth whitening options, using some viewers as patients, while the show's hosts judged the results. Our treatment got a five star rating and we had over 500 calls in the next two days and over 100 new patients coming in for treatment. Some hadn't seen a dentist in over ten years and were more than happy to spend $600 to whiten their teeth 'as seen on TV'. It is scary how much influence the TV has on people's choices.

96% of adults believe an attractive smile makes a person more appealing to the opposite sex. Three-quarters (74%) of adults feel an unattractive smile can hurt a person's chances of career success.[17]

Connected population

In the past it took someone like Tom Cruise to change his smile to get massive media attention. Now, with the power of social networking, news of even the average Joe having a dental procedure can spread like wildfire. Take a look at 'David after Dentist' on YouTube—this is a seven-year-old boy after a trip to the dentist and it has had over 80 million views! It is said that most people know about 250 people. If you follow on from Frigyes Karinthy's work on the six degrees of separation, you can't be sure that the patient that you have kept waiting 20 minutes for their appointment is not tweeting how rubbish your clinic is to his 250 Twitter followers (there are 175 million users globally). You have no control over what he says and who reads it, and it's potentially out there forever.

The reverse is also true, of course. One of the great things in my opinion about Google is that just when the techies have worked out its algorithm for how it ranks its searches, it changes again. The algorithm assigns an 'importance' value to each web page and gives it a rank to determine how useful it is. What Google tries to do is give its users relevant, up-to-date information. If your website has decent content and is well established with reliable incoming links it will do well. Google is starting to rank video content and consumer reviews of your service, giving more power to the consumer to reward excellent service and penalise poor service. The internet is becoming more and more a two-way process. How long before independent dental comparison sites start springing up, just like the sites that compare motor insurance and loans? How will you measure up? Stop now and Google your practice and your name. What comes up?

Social media has been mobile for a while with smartphones, but now with services like Facebook Places, Gowalla and Foursquare it is also location-based. Patients can mark they are at your clinic (make sure you get it listed as a business) and see who else is also checked in. If you visit a business a number of times in a period you get the privilege of being 'the major' of that location and get offered extra benefits such as free tooth whitening gel.

Bow Lane was the first dental practice in the world to develop an iPhone app. You can download this app right now—type in 'Bow Lane' on the iTunes store.

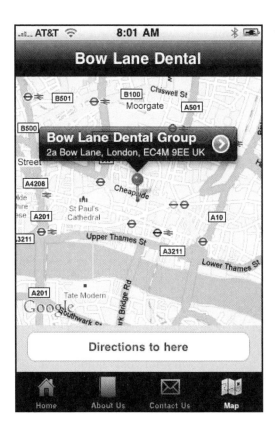

Why a dental practice app?

As a dentist, it is another way of communicating with my patients in a way that is convenient for them. Imagine that you have broken a front tooth and are searching for a dentist to fix it. Using the iPhone , or iPad, you can see how far the practice is from your current location.

You can also request an appointment and receive confirmation of availability by text. With built-in satellite mapping, you can then be walked step by step to the door—no excuse for being late. If you are on the train, it will tell you which stop to get off at (and while you are travelling, you may as well complete the online medical history questionnaire). You can watch a video featuring your chosen dentist, and be left with the feeling that you are already like old friends by the time you meet.

You have a great experience; no need to fumble to add all the contact details to your address book. One touch and it is all there. You sign up for the practice newsletters, which are emailed to you, and every time you launch the app the latest special offer or treatment shows up on the home page.

Main features of the free app are:

- Patients can be directed straight to your practice
- Special offers are pushed onto their phone
- They can watch videos of all the practice team
- They can see all the latest dental procedures explained
- They can fill in the new patient questionnaire and request an appointment on the go

How to keep up

I find one of the best ways to keep up with new developments is to subscribe to newsletters or blogs such as Springwise and Trendhunter. Most of them are free. Ask younger team members about the latest trends. Often your local dental organisation has a media alert service where they will send you, via email, all the dental related stores. The British Dental Association has a media alert service for its members. Check to see if your local dental association also offers this tool.

Another way is to use Really Simple Syndication (RSS). RSS is a way of aggregating many sources of information into one place. You can stay informed with the latest content and save time by not needing to visit multiple websites.

Don't forget to survey your patients. As I mentioned earlier, I use surveys a lot. I tend to focus my questions on three key areas:

- What they like about us
- What they hate about us
- What we could do better

If you would like some of my sample questions please sign up on www.jamesgoolnik.com and I will send you samples.

Other industries

It is easy to just look at the dental market without stepping back and seeing the wider picture. You yourself are a consumer in so many other areas. What excites you about a particular gym, for example—why do you go there? Visit the best health spa in your area and see what they do. Use all your senses. What does it smell like? How do you feel when you walk in the door? They may use thermostatically controlled oil burners to produce calming smells—perhaps that is something that could be used in your treatment rooms to banish that dental surgery smell.

Think about the best customer service experiences you have had recently, the ones you told your friends about. Why were they so special? Was it one thing they did or just the way you were taken care of? You know they have a system but it still makes you feel special. Perhaps you like the goody bags on the business class airline. Why not make something similar for your new patient welcome packs? Make your patient feel welcomed and special and give them something unique that they will talk to their friends about. We give all our patients lip balms after their appointments. It is has sun protection factor 30, smells gorgeous and is in our vibrant purple colour. Often patients cheekily ask for another one to give their work colleagues. It's great marketing.

You're the professional

Don't forget that one of the best ways of finding out about new techniques and products is from our professional network. Visiting trade shows is not only a great way to catch up with what the trade is bringing out, but also to connect with colleagues. Visiting conferences where there is a topic you are interested in will guarantee that you meet other like-minded professionals. The question "What's new?" tends to open up a plethora of opinions.

Increasingly your network is online, with communities such as Dentaltown and GDPUK where you can post questions and get a variety of opinions. I find it hard to gauge the reliability of some of the advice as it is mostly nameless and people tend to post what they are happy for the community to see; they may say something different face to face.

Also reading journals will help keep you up to date. CPD is mandatory if you want to continue to practise dentistry, so why not be picky in what CPD you choose?

Brush strokes:

- Google your name

- Ask your patients to review you on Google

- Get your practice listed on Facebook Places, Gowalla and Foursquare

- Start drafting your survey questions

- Subscribe to interesting blogs

- Be choosy with your CPD

9 Know and drive your market

It's not enough to be the best at what you do; you must
be perceived to be the only one who does what you do.

Jerry Garcia

I know it's boring, but research pays off. I remember when I was
thinking of setting up on my own I got a big map of London and
thought "Where do I want to work? Which areas do I know and
would enjoy working in?" I narrowed the search to Kensington &
Chelsea (affluent shopping district) and the City of London (the
financial heart of London). Then using Yellow Pages, the internet
and phone calls I plotted every existing dental practice in these
areas. From phone calls and asking dental colleagues I got to find
out how big a clinic was, who owned it (rough age, so how likely

to be close to retiring?) and what sort of dentistry they delivered. It took me about a year but I realised there was no-one in these areas who delivered the types of dentistry that I had planned.

After spending lots of time in these areas, there was something about the buzz of the City of London that attracted me, so I instructed a local agent to look for suitable premises. At the same time I wrote to all the targeted practices, seeing if they had plans to sell in the next 12 months. I got a great response, having sent hand-written letters to the principal dentists explaining that I had the funds and was interested in their practice if they were considering selling. After seeing five or six, I realised that it would be cheaper in the long run to start from scratch rather than modify an existing practice.

Once you know what sort of dentistry you want to deliver and have the entire picture in your head, go for it! Plenty of people have been passionate about an idea and opened up a new market that previously didn't exist. Think of Kindle and electronic books, or Lingual Braces in dentistry.

What's your niche?

A niche is a subset of the main market. It is highly focused. In theory the better you know and target your patients, the narrower your niche and the lower the risk of your patients being poached by the competition. For example, you may just treat referrals from dentists of very nervous patients needing root canal treatment. Or you could be a clinic that just treats HIV-positive patients with dental emergencies where no appointments are necessary, referring them on once immediate care has been given. These two clinics would be positioned very differently and marketed very differently. It is much harder to be different if you are a dental clinic that treats everyone. You will be the dental equivalent of vanilla ice cream and we all know how hard it is to choose which brand of vanilla. People usually end up choosing on price alone. The next time you go to the supermarket, a different brand is on sale and that is the end of your customer loyalty. Doing everything is:

a) Confusing for the customer

b) Difficult to market

c) Hard to focus for the team

d) Exhausting!

When you're one of a kind there's NO competition.

An easy way to start to discover what your niche is or where your strengths lie is a good old-fashioned brainstorming session.

I start with the basic question "Why do patients come to see us?" To get the best out of this you need to be strict on a few rules:

- Do it off-site, away from your working environment, ideally somewhere with no distractions. I remember one of my best sessions was with Roy Moed in his 'white room'.

This room is all white with one large window. There are no distractions. The room is basically one large whiteboard; you can write all over the walls in multicolour pens. Once you get started it is great fun and the child in everyone comes out. I find I can do this for about 45 minutes, then I need a break from the room.

- Write down every suggestion. Nothing is too obvious or stupid. You want to create an atmosphere where everyone is equal and deserves to be listened to. Don't debate each idea yet. Just write them all down.

- Once you get the ideas down, use another part of the whiteboard or flip chart to list the top ten that resonate with the whole team.

If you haven't started the business yet or there is just you, I would start with the thought that you are a fly on the wall in your local gym. One of your patients is telling a friend who is looking for a new dentist why he comes to your practice. What would you love him to say about your practice?

After I completed a short course of treatment with a new patient I asked him if he could tell me what he liked about this practice and why he came back to complete treatment when he had been putting it off for years. He said he didn't feel judged or chastised by the team for not taking care of his mouth previously, and he loved the fact he could watch a DVD while having treatment. He felt coming to see us was like taking a business class flight, with all the goodies and the feeling of being looked after.

We talked earlier about surveying your patients. Take a good look at the optional comment boxes. This is where you will find out what is special about your clinic and what you can build on.

Remember, you need to make sure ALL your business decisions are made with your niche in mind. For example, one of your clinicians goes on a facial aesthetics course and wants to offer fillers and Botox. It may even be a service that some of your patients want. But does it fit with your practice ethos? If not and there is demand, why not develop a strategic alliance with a plastic surgery clinic nearby? Just remember it is important to meet ALL the businesses that you are recommending to your patients. They need to at least meet your level of customer service and have a similar ethos. Once you have built that relationship we will talk later about nurturing it.

Advertising return on investment

I found placing advertisements in local magazines and newspapers to be a waste of time. The return on investment is not good enough (I would want at least five times the advertising cost). If you do decide to place any kind of advertising, these are my takeaways:

- Don't let the media company design the advert. It will be generic, boring and not be consistent with your brand. Get your graphic designers to work to the media spec.

- Don't say yes to their first offer—come to think of it, their second or third offer either. The first pitch is the so-called 'rate card'. Only a mug pays rate card. This is the opening price to negotiate from. As the deadline gets closer the rate will come down. Mention you are planning a series of placements with the right publication.

- Pick your position in the publication and get it put in the contract. Studies show right-hand pages have more impact.

- Get previous copies of the publication. Call other advertisers and ask them what the return has been.

Start to shout

It's no good being the best endodontist in your city if no-one knows about it. I believe that the most authentic way of doing this is by word of mouth. How are you going to get people to start talking in the first place?

This picture overleaf is a simplistic explanation of the difference between marketing, PR, advertising and branding. I want you to have nailed your niche and be working on marketing so your PR is carried out by your brand ambassadors—your patients and team members.

It is all about story telling, and it's much more effective if other people are telling your stories. Otherwise it looks like bragging.

An easy way to start to shout is when you have a new treatment. For example, you have been on a course and are offering no-prep veneers. The process to go through is:

1. Do a few cases first to make sure you are knowledgeable in the technique and have all the materials and laboratory support you need. Give a few cards to these patients and give them permission to talk about what they had to their friends and family. Ask if they would be happy to be interviewed if selected media contacts want a quote from them.

2. At one of your staff meetings explain what's different and hand everyone a cheat sheet with bullet points of the procedure so that they can answer any questions.

3. Add the service to the website, with before and after pictures from your completed cases.

4. Write a short press release (we talked about this in Chapter 3) and send it to local media by email and fax.

5. Write a piece to go in the next e-newsletter

Another way to shout is to volunteer to be a media spokesperson. This can be as simple as writing a short article about a new procedure that is targeted to the audience of that media. They will then see if you understand their specific audience, can write and, crucially, come up with short soundbites that engage with their audience. At the bottom of the article explain you are available for interview. In the majority of cases you will not get paid for this. They may cover travelling expenses if you are lucky, but you do not speak to the media for the money.

It is all about credibility, and it's fun once you get over the initial nerves. I don't care how many times you have been on television or the radio, it always starts with that feeling in your stomach. It gives you your edge and makes you human. Once you do a good job for them, tell them you enjoyed it and would be happy to help with ANY dental-related feature they come across in the future. Remember, they are looking for quick responses and unless it is a monthly magazine they often have very short deadlines. The secret is to respond quickly. If you cannot help personally, help them find someone who can. That way you become their 'go-to guy'!

Being congruent and authentic is critical. People can smell when they are being sold a line, especially when it's not your line. I remember a few years back elevator pitches were in fashion. Business gurus helped people write their pitches and when you asked a dentist what they did you would invariably see their lips moving but hear someone else's words coming out. It's about you: people want to hear what you have to say about yourself. What do you believe and why?

Blogging

So you have a voice and feel passionate about something. A good way of getting your voice out there is to write a blog. Now with programs such as WordPress (www.wordpress.org) it's free and easy to get your blog up and running.

Before you put this book down and start blogging (I know you are champing at the bit to get started) think first about who your audience is. Are you writing to the general public or is it to the profession? Your voice and your topics need to be different, depending on who you are talking to. It is hard enough keeping a blog fresh and up-to-date without trying to do both. We talked earlier about your niche and using your time in an effective way. Who do you want to read your blog?

Six top tips for blogging:

1. Make it fun! Otherwise why bother?

2. Make the headlines sticky. People have a short attention span online, so grab them fast, then give them something valuable which will make them want to stay.

3. Update it regularly, at least once a week.

4. Respect copyright. If you are going to republish someone else's work, ask their permission first and quote the source.

5. Use multimedia—photographs, links to videos and other relevant sites.

6. Take part in the conversation. Remember, if you allow comments (which I think is a good idea) you are responsible for all the material that is published on your blog.

Looking for inspiration?

Never be afraid to fail. I have failed lots of times. The hard part is to acknowledge to yourself that it is not working, stop, learn and move on. Some on the world's most successful people have had catastrophic failures. The hit TV show *The Office* was nearly never broadcast. It did not meet the BBC's standard funding criteria for new programmes and at one point looked dead in the water. Luckily the BBC had set up a 'gambling fund' which it used to fund experimental programmes and bet on risky ideas. *The Office* only went ahead because of this gambling fund.

20% Time

Google has a '20% time' culture. Simply put, employees get one fifth of their time to work on projects of their own choosing. If you want innovation, it's critical that people are able to work on ideas that are unapproved or even thought to be stupid. The real value is not the time, but rather the licence it gives to work on things that aren't obviously important. People at Google work very hard and it is not as if they shut down early on a Friday. It's more a case of 'if you have an idea you should work on it, though not to the detriment of your other responsibilities'. This 20% time is protected, but protected by the individual rather than by the managers. How could this work in your practice? Could you give your receptionists time to intimately observe the patients and see what they are missing by being 'in' the day-to-day of the job. Could they try different things and see what fails? After all, life is one big experiment. Perhaps they could get one their friends to be a mystery shopper to test your level of customer service.

How to fail

In business I find the hardest bit is to let people know that you failed. In my mind I see them laughing at me. In reality that has never happened. I find being honest works much better, acknowledging something has not worked but saying you are dedicated to getting it right by working together. In dentistry ALL our treatment will ultimately fail. It is just a matter of whether the patient dies before it fails or not!

If I have tried to whiten a patient's teeth and they have followed all the aftercare instructions and I did not achieve a result that we are both happy with, I say "I really tried to get your teeth to the colour we had both chosen but it was not possible. I am really sorry and would like to offer you full refund." That's the best PR you can get. It instantly defuses any potential situation. They tell their friends that you are honest and put your patient's results first. Often they come back for more extensive treatment such as veneers. Treating our patients as we would like to be treated is our baseline.

Don't keep flogging a dead horse. I was the European sales agent for the Supersmile range of oral hygiene products. I thought they were great and was given the UK rights with certain targets which would open up the European market if I performed. At the time I did not account for currency exchange rates. Once we sold the initial batch and came to reorder, the currency fluctuation meant that it was going to be 50% more expensive. I had not allowed any flexibility in my pricing model and suddenly I was making 10 cents on a tube of toothpaste. It was not the manufacturer's problem—they wanted their margin and I was a new business. I did not believe in my heart that the UK market would take any higher pricing and decided to cut my losses and forfeit my contract. It was my first foray into selling dental products to the public and I learned never to get the profit margins wrong again.

Measure it!

The management consultant Peter Drucker said that what gets measured improves. Human nature is such that if we are asked to measure something we notice it more and tend to become engaged in improving whatever we are measuring. Unless you have a way of assessing performance, how do you know if you are improving? If you do not measure a set of figures you can only guess whether the performance has increased, and by how much. If you just measure profitability without a breakdown, how do you know if it has increased because your sales went up or your expenses went down?

A classic example is if you want to lose weight. First of all you have the daily measurements, whether it is the scales or tape measure. Then it's the 'before' photographs (put them in a place that you can see them daily) then it's telling other people that you are going to hit this target by a specific date. That makes you accountable.

It's the same in dentistry. I want to hit 35% profitability by year end. I mention the profit percentage daily at the morning huddle. I write the figure on the board in the staff room. I give the team a target date and an incentive to succeed: I tell them I will take them all out to Gordon Ramsay's latest restaurant when we hit it. Do you think the team will be engaged now?

I have been involved with Henry Schein testing their Thrive product. It is a tag-on service to their practice management software that helps measure your practice's financial performance. They look at ten key performance indictors (KPIs) that give you a snapshot of your performance and then co-monitor the improvements over the six-month programme. Once you get over the learning curve (as with any new bit of software) and enter the data in the correct format it gives very useable results:

1. Chair time utilisation. Do you know how many of the available hours in your clinic are actually used? Could you sub-let one room if you are effectively not using it?

2. Failure to attend. What is your cancellation rate? How many patients miss their appointments? You still need to pay your team.

3. Do you know your top ten invoiced treatments? Think Pareto's Principle—the 80:20 rule. 80% of your revenue is derived for 20% of your available treatments. A small increase in the fees for one of those top 20% treatments can make a massive difference.

4. Top referral sources. Do you know who they are, and are you rewarding them and making it easy for them to continue doing so?

5. Earnings per hour. Compare clinicians to see who is more effective. Then look at expenses to find out who is more profitable.

6. Forward cover. Do you have a short-notice cancellation list that can fill gaps in your schedule?

7. Number of new patients. This is a sign of a growing and thriving practice. You will get natural attrition because patients move away from the area or die. You need to be constantly adding new patients. In other industries this is called the churn rate.

8. How effective is your recall? Are patients coming back, and how long does it take for them to return? Which clinician is the most effective? What are they doing differently?

9. Fee per patient. How much revenue are you generating per patient? Is this increasing?

10. Patient debt. How is your collection rate? How long does it take for your average patient to pay you? You are not in the finance industry!

Reviewing your KPIs will not only improve your profitability but also your efficiency. You do not have to use the Thrive software—you can even use pen and paper—but there is NO excuse for not measuring them. Don't rely on your accountant to tell you how you are doing; that is in the past. You need a finger on the pulse and know day by day how you are doing, what is working and what is not.

The really exciting thing about all this data is that you can anonymise it and then create benchmarks to compare your performance with others. There is nothing better than a yardstick that shows you are underperforming in a certain area to get you to make a change. In the 21st century data is king.

Brush strokes:

- What's your niche?

- What would you love your patients to say about your practice?

- Write a short article and send it to your local media

- You're a dentist—but what do you really do, and why?

- Start an authentic blog

- Mystery shopper

- How could you implement 20% time?

- What are your KPIs? Measure them regularly!

10 Develop a support network

Coming together is a beginning. Keeping together is progress. Working together is success.
Henry Ford

Over time I have realised that a lot of dentists have similar character traits. They can be very driven people who are not great with criticism. Sure, you can do it on your own. But why not learn sitting on the shoulders of others? I firmly believe in growing your network and living life by helping others.

Relationships need to be mutually beneficial over time, otherwise one party starts to harbour doubts about the equality of the relationship. I think "How can I add value to this person" and often it's the simple things like connecting them to a person who may be a mutually beneficial business connection. Perhaps you know a good electrician?

Over time you will have built up a great network of people with different skills who you enjoy spending time with. These people you may mentor and they may mentor you. Think of it as your own board of advisors. You are considering investing money in a new project; you draw up a simple business plan and get them round for dinner and pitch it to them on a confidential basis, getting them to ask you any questions and give you their gut feelings based on experience.

It doesn't have to be informal and unpaid. Some people are semi-retired and would love to be on board as a non-executive officer, maybe meeting up twice a year and being paid a small fee as an advisor. You may find you need a business manager at your clinic; you can use this support network to help you find the right person. We talked earlier about business coaches. Just about every professional sportsperson has a coach. Why should business people be any different?

What's its function?

Your support network, or as I will call it from now on, your board of advisors has four main functions:

a) Accountability. I told my board about this book. Each time I saw them they asked how it was going, did I need any help with contacts in the publishing world, when would it be out? They all wanted signed copies. For me, that was a great driver to make sure it was actually published.

b) Extend your network. They know all about you and what your niche is. Whenever dentistry comes up in conversation they will mention your name. These people know other people and it increases the chances that you will be offered other opportunities. Have you noticed how some people keep appearing in different places? They are the well connected ones.

c) Provide missing skills. This mini-board of directors may have HR skills, corporate finance skills and so on. That could be useful at various times in your career. It is also beneficial for them. You not only give them access to the world of dental care, you are also likely to have access to the medical profession in a way they are unlikely to have. I remember when I starting selling products to dentists I realised I knew nothing about telesales. We could all sell face to face, but selling over the phone is a completely different skill. One of my friends, Elliot Jacobs, runs a very successful stationery company and he has a team of telesales people. I was able to bounce some ideas of him and he even lent me a freelance salesperson to get us off the ground and help teach two of our team.

d) Emotional support. Change is scary and just having them there at the end of a phone, especially if they have been through a similar experience, really does help. You can learn from their mistakes; they know what the warning signs are. We had to get rid of one member of our hygiene team as she did not fit in and her time-keeping was erratic. I asked my board of advisors and one of them had had a similar problem; he was able to email me a series of letters to go through the disciplinary procedure and avoid unnecessary legal complications.

How to find the right people

This will seem very daunting at first, but you probably have these people in your contacts already—you just did not think of them in a board capacity. You may also be guilty of not reciprocating their friendship and only contacting them when you need something. There is a certain etiquette to apply:

1. Reply promptly to any contact, even if it is just to say you will be in touch again. It is frustrating for people not to know if their email has been overlooked or just ignored!

2. If you get a connection from your network, always include them in the 'BCC' section when you follow it up, then take them out of the loop on the follow-up conversation.

3. Spell-check before hitting Send. It just looks lazy or, even worse, ignorant if your messages are full of spelling mistakes.

4. Once you have made that connection, remember you are not only representing yourself but also your board.

Perhaps you are looking to set up a chain of dental practices and need someone with experience of something similar, for example running a chain of franchises. You will need to spend a bit of time drawing up the ideal specification so you know when you find them.

It is important to think outside of the dental market, as it is really the business skills that you require. Look at your contacts now; see who would fit the bill. If you are missing some, you have a few avenues:

a) Send an email to your most connected people, the ones most likely to know someone. Looking at six degrees of separation, you should be able to get a personal introduction to anyone on the planet in six connections or less. Some people naturally have a large pool of connections. I remember I was having a visa problem at Heathrow and the check-in staff would not let me fly to Dubai. Just one phone call to one of my connected friends, Ajay Mipuri, and I had the Emirati consulate on the phone 45 minutes later. They managed to sort out my visa to fly the next day. That friend got a hamper of muffins delivered the next day.

b) Ask. If you believe in 'The Secret', ask and you will receive. The more people you mention your quest to, the quicker it is likely to be answered.

c) Social networking. Facebook is great at putting mini job descriptions up and seeing if you get a response. It is free and instant.

d) Use an agency to help your search. With your specification they can tell if they have someone on their books and help you get the remuneration right. Obviously it depends on the level of experience and number of hours you require.

e) Business networking. Try using a network like BNI, the largest business referral organisation in the world, or Toastmasters to let people know you are looking for someone. Each country has a specific networking organisation or breakfast clubs where people from different industries come to share resources.

f) Entrepreneurs' Organization (EO). This is a dynamic global network of more than 7,500 business owners in 38 countries. EO (www.eonetwork.org) is the catalyst that enables entrepreneurs to learn and grow from each other, leading to improved business success and an enriched personal life. Membership is by invitation only. I find the most useful aspect of membership is my forum. This is a group of eight entrepreneurs who meet monthly for peer-to-peer learning and support, utilising special protocols to develop a trusting environment in which we can safely explore business and personal growth issues. During forum meetings we discuss the 5% of stuff that we don't share with the world, the triumphs and tragedies of life as an entrepreneur.

g) Other country-specific services such as Business Link. This gives free business advice and support, available online at www.businesslink.gov.uk and through local advisers.

Growing and nurturing your network

So you've got this great network, what next? As the expression goes, water it otherwise it will die. I would suggest at least monthly emails or calls just to check in. You need to physically meet up at least twice a year for a mini-board meeting. This board meeting is a chance for you all to get updates on each other's progress and refocus for the six months ahead. At certain times you may have much more frequent contact, but you all need to be at least in each other's subconscious.

Often with busy people it is hard to tie down a convenient time for everyone to meet. I use Doodle (www.doodle.com) which is great free online tool to schedule a time and day which is best for everyone. You log in and set the available days and then send the link to all the board. They tick the times they are free and the one with the most ticks is the new date.

You may or may not be paying your advisors directly. An average non-executive officer will get at least $1,500 per day plus expenses. Most of these people do not do it for the money as their daily rate is a lot higher than that. They do it for a challenge, they see you in them and they want to give back. I suggest you consider other methods of saying you value them:

1. Letters. When did you last write a thank you note? Probably after your wedding! When did you last receive one? Probably from a child who was coerced into it by their parents. You always remember your last hand-written unexpected note. Make sure your note is the last one they remember. In the era of digital instant communication, nothing quite says thank you better than a letter.

2. Refer business to them. If you know somebody who would benefit from a product or service that they represent, then refer them a new customer.

3. Birthdays. No matter how old you are, your birthday is always special. I remember one of my forum mates who was 38 mentioned he did not get any cards for his birthday, not even from his wife and two children. The following year I reminded the rest of the forum and at least he had seven cards that year. With Outlook Reminders and Facebook you have no excuse to forget again.

4. Find out their passions. Perhaps support their favourite charity, get tickets to their favourite theatre, anything that suggests you have put some effort into finding out what makes them tick.

5. In your book (you know you want to write one—81% of all Americans say they will write a book one day). Don't forget to acknowledge all the people who helped you along the way.

Brush strokes:

- Think how you can help others first

- Draw up a specification for your board of directors

- Look at your contact book and start recruiting

- Next time one of your friends does something beyond the call of duty send them a hand-written thank you note and watch their reaction

- Nurture your network or watch it die

- Set up your next meeting through Doodle

Clinical trends

Don't keep following trends—innovate and start them!
James Goolnik

So what are we seeing clinically? These trends have been gathered from dental supply houses, academics, laboratories, private practices and trade organisations. More than ever before, consumers know what they want and how and where to get it. Stories travel faster. The number one factor motivating the purchase of a new technology for a dentist is peer recommendation, followed by lectures/seminars.

One-visit dentistry

The fact is we have less free time than ever before and more demands on our time. Dentistry for most people is a necessary evil and no matter how great friends you are with your patients, they don't want to see you more than they need to. How great would it be if they came in with an issue and you were able to solve it then and there with no follow-up appointment needed.

This is the basis of CAD:CAM dentistry; the most successful proponent of this is CEREC. How cool is it? One anaesthetic, no impressions, no temporaries and all done in one visit. I know some offices that have the milling machine (the bit that cuts the porcelain restoration) in the patient lounge for patients to watch. The latest machine from Sirona has a cool blue light and is quite mesmerising to watch. It is a great conversation starter for new patients. The future is more lifelike restorations, constructed instantly, with less learning curve for the clinician, using a handheld optical scanner to capture an accurate model of the whole mouth no matter what materials are present.

Implant Dentistry

The dental implant market was estimated to be around $3.2 billion globally in 2010.[18] In order for it to grow it needs to be simpler and offer patients what they really want: teeth in a day with one surgical procedure.

The possibilities for future applications of CAD:CAM are even more extensive when you combine them with CT scanners to plan implant treatment. The planning of the final position of the restoration can be added to the CT software image to ensure that the position of the implant is ideal. Surgical guide stents can be processed directly from this planning software to aid in the correct surgical placement. The actual prostheses will soon be able to be constructed at this planning stage, to be fitted immediately on placement of implants without any conventional impressions being taken. It is also likely that the drilling process will be computer-guided from this information. Combining this with digital photography and manipulation, smile design principles can be put into the mix.

User interfaces

Look at how computer gaming has changed since the launch of the Xbox in 2001. With immersive technologies we have a controller-free games experience. It won't be long before the technology catches up in dentistry, due to the dramatic drop in the cost of sensors. The interface will be virtual, rather like in the film *Minority Report*, further improving our cross-infection protocol.

We will be able to harness the power of the rest of the team, especially the hygiene department. With their expanded duties they will be offering more preventive dentistry and restorations, freeing up the dentists to screen new patients, treatment plan and carry out the more complex restorative dentistry. Most hygienists have better rapport and communication skills than the rest of the dental team and are ideally placed to help build trust and educate patients. With more of them learning about aesthetics and having clinical photography skills, they are starting to branch into facial aesthetics, Botox and fillers where local regulations allow. Gone are the days when they were just the teeth cleaners!

Tooth whitening

Who does not want a whiter smile? According to Mintel, over a quarter (26%) of the UK population who visited their dentist had cosmetic dental treatments.[19] Teeth whitening was the most popular treatment (31%), followed by white fillings (30%), crowns or bridges (21%) and veneers (18%). The age analysis showed that people in the 25-34 age group were the most likely to have had teeth whitening.

Don't drill my teeth

Let's face it, no-one likes the dental drill. It was invented by an English dentist, George Fellows Harrington, in 1864. This is the object that most people's fear of the dentist stems from, and it is usually the shrill sound that starts them off. As we know, only 75% of the developed world's population actually visit the dentist. Of the people who do, over 48% experience extreme to moderate anxiety. This level is higher among young adults (16-34 years old) and more prevalent in women.[14]

Having a tooth drilled and having an injection are the two aspects that cause them anxiety. If you tell people "We can fix your teeth without using the drill and often no anaesthesia" you can see them visibly relax. So what options do we have now and what's exciting in the future?

Dental Lasers

I did my thesis on lasers at the Eastman Dental Institute and they are great. But unfortunately hard tissue lasers cannot remove metal-based filling materials and they are still very expensive. I love my soft tissue laser and couldn't practise dentistry now without it. Despite this only about 3% of dentists use lasers, mainly due to cost. This is changing. With prices set to fall and the delivery systems getting smaller and more portable, practices will start to see the benefits of having a hard tissue laser. There are even rumours of them being able to cut amalgam and other metals.[20]

Fast orthodontics

When you mention orthodontics to a patient they instantly think of fixed braces in place for a year or more, and switch off. If you phrase the question a bit differently—"If I could give you straight teeth without anyone knowing you were wearing an appliance, would you say yes?"—their reaction is totally different. There are now a myriad of techniques and appliances to straighten teeth in more aesthetic and faster ways:

a) Lingual braces—braces on the insides of the teeth. They function in exactly the same way as conventional labial braces but are almost invisible. They do take some getting used to regarding speech and eating (most of my patients actually like the fact that they may lose some weight). The time scale is the same as for conventional braces but the patient is less keen to have them removed as they are not on show.

b) Six Month Smiles (6MS). This is more like conventional braces, using clear brackets and tooth-coloured wires but just moving the anterior teeth. Treatment time is on average four to nine months.

c) Inman Aligner. Very similar principle to 6MS but using a removable appliance to move just the anterior teeth. The more the aligner is worn, the quicker the movement (ideally removed only when eating or cleaning your teeth) but on average in just four months the front teeth are straight. Both 6MS and Inman are great for post-orthodontic relapse cases.

d) Invisalign. This is a clear aligner system that has revolutionised the orthodontic market. Never before has such an extensive public campaign been waged regarding orthodontics. In 2009 Align Tech spent over $110 million on marketing.

None of these systems is perfect and they ALL need permanent retention to prevent relapse. Thanks to the increased public awareness of orthodontic options from companies such as Invisalign, shows like *Ugly Betty* and the fact that more general dentists are offering simple orthodontics, uptake is growing. Invisalign are now starting to aggressively market to teenagers, making it the orthodontic option of choice for the teen.

Over 730,000 patients have used or are using Invisalign.[21] This is a 75% increase in the last five years. There are close to 36,000 US practitioners (orthodontists and other medical or dental professionals) trained in Invisalign treatment, and just over 48,000 worldwide.

Currently 76% of dental practices in the UK do not offer orthodontics at their practice.[16]

No-prep veneers

Despite popular belief, dental veneers were invented by a Californian dentist named Charles Pincus in 1937. He used them for Hollywood stars and they were basically part of the make-up artist's box of tricks; they would stay on your teeth for most of the day. Luckily adhesive technology has moved on and today's well bonded veneer should be semi-permanent. In the 1980s veneers started to become more mainstream and dentists and their patients saw them as a quick and easy way of dramatically improving a smile without necessitating the removal of healthy tooth structure. There was a massive surge in the number of root canal treatments as the teeth were often over-prepared in an effort to correct the underlying crookedness. A large proportion of the dental profession saw the dollar signs and did not think of the long-term consequences. We were in the 'now' culture and everything had to be done yesterday. More dental practices jumped on the bandwagon; the less skilled operators, seduced by the dazzling transformations and by celebrity dentistry, thought "This looks easy." Without following the principles of sound dentistry and respect for the occlusion, gingival architecture and dental tissue, there was serious overtreatment.

That has changed with the advent of faster orthodontics so teeth can be moved into optimal positions with little or no tooth reduction. Dentists have come back to the planning stage and are now using photography, diagnostic mock-ups and better communication with the laboratory technicians to give an aesthetic, functional, minimally invasive result.

In 2003 the British Academy of Cosmetic Dentists was formed after it was realised there was a significant gap in the training of aesthetic dentistry and a huge demand in the market. Our colleagues traditionally went to the US to the American Academy of Cosmetic Dentistry and other aesthetic dental training institutes. Thankfully now there are many excellent global training facilities for the aesthetic dentist. Newly qualified dentists still want to practise aesthetic dentistry but they need to have a solid knowledge of the cornerstones of dentistry before embarking on what is often elective dentistry.

Having an orthodontist and dental laboratory on site, I am lucky to be able to co-treatment plan with my patients on how to improve their smile and function, with only minimal reduction in tooth tissue. Because of the way minimal preparation veneers were marketed, dentists thought they were even easier—you just took a mould, decided on a final shade and eight beautiful veneers were ready to fit in two weeks. I would never do a minimal prep veneer case without the patient test-driving their new smile to make sure they are happy with the aesthetics and function. This can be achieved either directly in the mouth with composite mock-ups or using a diagnostic wax-up and fitting acrylic resin temporaries.

Dr Dennis Wells, whose Nashville Center for Aesthetic Dentistry pioneered Durathins, has realised that treatment planning is critical and they will not let you use their laboratory without attending a certification course. Lumineers have also used this model. They agree there is no such thing as non-preparation reversible veneers because if you etch and bond a tooth you will always alter the enamel. But these veneers are the future as they have better bond strength, being almost entirely bonded to enamel. There is no sensitivity and zero chance of causing the tooth to become non-vital and require root canal treatment.

Bonding

With the better colour stability, polishablility and wear characteristics of modern composite resins, these are great options to improve a smile. Often at the end of orthodontic treatment, with a few additions of bonding and some reshaping, you can take a good smile and turn it into a great smile. Composite materials are probably the most tweaked and enhanced by the manufacturers of all restorative materials. What we were using three years ago is probably not even manufactured any more. There are flowable materials out there such as Smart Dentine Replacement from Dentsply that flows but slumps to allow you to use bulk linings underneath restoration quickly with no sensitivity. They are getting closer to the wear and aesthetic characteristics of natural tooth tissues and can be easily repaired.

The manufacturers will be pushing nanotechnology and low shrink compounds. There seems to be a trend towards a two tier system, a user-friendly one for the masses and a higher-end artistic version to appeal to the more aesthetic dentists who like to mimic nature.

Bleaching

This is the most requested dental procedure and the one that brings in people who have never visited the dentist in their lives before. With massive consumer campaigns from toothpaste companies, Britesmile advertisements and walk-in tooth whitening clinics, it has made dentistry more accessible. Despite this, 22% of all dental practices in the UK do not offer tooth whitening.[16]

One of my in-office whitening patients was a well educated medical doctor who had recently been divorced and had not really bothered about his teeth previously. He had a few missing posterior teeth and signs of occlusal wear. We whitened his teeth and he then went on to have adult orthodontics, implants and some veneers, a total of $30,000 worth of dentistry—all because he saw the Britesmile ad in his local paper. You never know when a patient will convert from one specific treatment—a whitening, broken tooth or hygiene appointment—to more extensive treatment. My record so far is nine years between one visit dentistry and a reconstruction. You should treat EVERY patient as if they are going to be a long term patient and part of your family, no matter what they come in for.

Power or in-office whitening is getting faster, with the ideal of having the entire treatment completed in 30 minutes with zero sensitivity. Whatever your beliefs about the use of the light, it agrees with scientific principles that a chemical reaction is accelerated by heat, and these lights are excellent heat sources. Saying that, the trend is now moving away from the use of the light, with companies such as Discus Dental stopping production of the very successful Zoom lamp and concentrating their efforts on systems that do not need light acceleration, such as Dash.

Take-home kits have more comfortable trays with more active peroxide-based chemicals which activate when needed and have longer shelf lives. The chemicals have more desensitisers to reduce the biggest complication of tooth whitening, post-operative sensitivity. We use trays to best deliver potassium nitrate to reduce tooth sensitivity separately to a tooth whitening procedure, using Discus Relief gel worn for 20 minutes in a custom-made tray every day for one week prior to tooth whitening to 'preload' the dentine tubules, reducing tooth sensitivity in vulnerable patients.

Shop purchased products

The legality of these systems is different throughout the world. The biggest most researched global product is Procter and Gamble's Whitestrips. They have improved the adhesives with advanced seal and are again working on the formulation to reduce the wear time, sensitivity and unrefrigerated shelf life.

The big battle will be with all the non-dental professionals carrying out tooth whitening in unregulated premises, with poorly researched products, applied illegally. We have only ourselves to blame. That is because dentistry still seems an unwelcoming service delivered in scary clinical environments with what patients perceive as high fees. If only the dental profession could offer tooth whitening for $99 or £60 in a non-threatening environment with non-judgmental team members. In the UK the General Dental Council is bringing a test case against some beauticians for illegal practice of dentistry. Some practitioners are using chlorine dioxide gels to try to get around the law, but this chemical has a pH of 1 and will dissolve the surface of the tooth, causing permanent damage. The bottom line is that even if they use peanut butter to whiten their patients' teeth, they are practising dentistry illegally and should be prosecuted. I prefer to see dental therapists and hygienists being able to set up their own clinics and offer tooth whitening in a safe environment, referring on complex cases to their local dentist.

Refurbish my mouth

With the reduction in use of dental amalgam and more aesthetic materials that can be bonded to, we will see fewer restorations being entirely removed when they fail and only the areas of the restoration that need attention being repaired. Low dose digital radiographs, fluoride toothpaste and more regular dental visits show small areas of caries or chips can be repaired easily, often without the use of local anaesthetic. What better incentive for your patients than to tell them "We can repair your restorations for a fraction of the cost, in one visit, without injections, if you attend regularly for your maintenance appointment." You know that the more often a restoration is replaced the less tooth structure is left, so the more likely the patient is to have sensitivity and need root canal work and a cusp coverage restoration.

A few years ago if you damaged one of your car's alloy wheels you had to replace the whole wheel. Now you get a man come to you and repair the wheel while it is still on the car. The same rationale is creeping into dentistry.

Ceramic bonding systems are getting more predictable and with fewer steps. Our dental materials will be engineered to be easily and predictably repaired as they are expected to be in our patient's mouth for longer as our life expectancy increases. Human life expectancy rises about three months every year though we will probably feel less healthy.

In the past you would automatically cut a tooth for a crown when it was significantly broken down. Now we look to design the restoration to replace the missing tooth structure and rely more on our bonding systems to retain the restoration and seal the tooth from fluid and bacteria ingress. Onlays are much more conservative and often, if made from composite, they need less space and therefore less reduction of the natural tooth. With porcelain systems like e.max (lithium disilicate) less tooth tissue needs to be removed in order to give a hard-wearing aesthetic restoration.

Despite all our measures, sometimes the only solution is to remove a tooth. We are getting better at atraumatic removal and techniques to augment the bone and maintain the soft tissue levels. Columbia University is pioneering the growing of new teeth using stem cell research. Using tooth-shaped scaffolds with growth factors and proteins, they can grow a tooth in only nine weeks. The conventional wisdom that we have only two sets of teeth could soon be a thing of the past!

Decay management

In certain parts of the world caries is still a major issue. With the rising levels of obesity and processed foods it is a behavioural change which will take a while to address.

Caries is a preventable bacterial disease and education is our first port of call. There are increasing levels of adjuncts of the market, not only patient-applied at home but in-office fluoride treatments. Xylitol has been shown to help in the remineralisation of teeth and is a sugar substitute than does not cause caries. Manufacturers have used it successfully in mouthwash and chewing gum. There are over 28 million regular chewing gum users in the UK alone, with the USA being the largest consumer of chewing gum. The big problem is that most of it ends up on the sidewalks and it takes five years to degrade, so it is causing a very expensive clean up operation. There is a new product called Rev7 that tastes like a normal gum but will degrade into dust within six months. They are currently working on a Xylitol version.

No matter how much we do in our office, for a susceptible patient with the wrong diet we are fighting a losing battle. They get to expect dental treatment every time they visit the practice and everyone gets demoralised. There are tests available to identify the caries-susceptible patient and we can treat them more aggressively.

Companies like DMG have brought out products like Icon which is a chemical treatment to arrest caries using resin infiltration technology. They have developed a smooth and interproximal clinical kit and it is currently being trialled.

Some of the latest treatments may bring us a small respite but unless a lot of patients modify their diet we have no hope.

Brush strokes:

- How could you start practising one-visit dentistry in all areas?

- Offer orthodontic options to your patients

- Look at repairable materials

- Start using markers to identify caries and peridontitis susceptible patients

- Ask your technician about the latest porcelain systems

- Take at look at www.jamesgoolnik.com for my latest courses

12 What does the future hold?

I happened to come along in the music business when there was no trend.

Elvis Presley

When I speak to the trend setters in dentistry and visit other countries, what do I see going on in the dental market? It is fascinating how there is little to separate all the countries. Sure, the level of orthodontic treatment is different and the incidence of caries is different, but generally the picture is very similar. There is a definite feminisation of the dental workforce. In the UK 43% are female (up 5% on last year) and in the US it is 47% (up 7%). In the UK there is also a shift towards more Asian dentists.[5,6] Is this because dentistry is considered one of the safer degree subjects, with a vocation and a guaranteed job at the end? I think it is more that it is a very flexible profession that you can dip in and out of to have a family; you can work just one day a week or set up a global empire, depending on your fancy.

Some trends are driven by the economic climate. Less new equipment is being purchased now than previously, but more maintenance contracts are being taken out. Henry Schein, the largest provider of healthcare services, has seen a big uptake in servicing and preventive maintenance visits. People are realising that with regular planned maintenance their equipment lasts longer and does not break down.

Dentists are responding to their patients' changing economic circumstances by offering:

a) Extended treatment duration or treatment broken down into stages to help spread the cost.

b) Third party financing.

c) Discounts, especially if patients pay in advance—10% is not uncommon.

d) In-house financing. The practice takes on the risk but it is less embarrassing than the patient being refused credit by third parties.

Is this it? Otherwise know as work/life balance

There is a big shift towards part-time work. It is not uncommon to find not a single full-time clinician in the practice, and we are starting to see the same shift in the support team as well. Dentistry is great on a shift basis; it allows the patients more flexibility in appointment times and allows you to hire expertise when you need it. I see periodontists working just one day per month in up to 12 different practices. Imagine the Christmas parties!

Apparently dentistry is a very stressful profession, with high suicide rates and levels of alcoholism. I don't drink and have deliberately not taken out any life insurance so I am worth more alive! Perhaps it is because we are perfectionists and spend most of our time staring into someone's mouth, working on people who don't want to be there. They state we have easy access to drugs as well.

For me life is about giving your best, listening to your passions and following them. It's about balancing the four aspects of your life—work, family, couple time and time on your own. We have so many demands on our time now; with electronic communication you are connected 24/7. How about switching off that phone and having a night in with your family? Most so-called emergencies will sort themselves out on their own. I found the quicker I replied to emails the quicker people expected me to reply. With instant messaging now, they can see when you read them and even as you are typing back!

So, two quick exercises that I have modified over the years:

1. What are you truly passionate about? Ignore what's cool or not, remember this is about you. What gives you a big grin when you think about it? (come on, we're being serious). Dabble. I have tried loads of things and you never know what will spark your interest. Don't be afraid to stop if you lose interest. That's what's great about the internet—you can find groups interested in collecting toothpaste tube caps if you look hard enough.

2. If you KNEW you couldn't fail and those around you would FULLY support you, what would you do?

I have seen many successful practitioners with more than one office location but they all seem a little frazzled, so I decided to stay with one location, get it right and try to get more balance into my life. One of my associate dentists decided he liked life in Israel better for his young family. He also decided that his dental career in the UK was more satisfying and had better potential opportunities. He has been commuting from Israel for the past two years, working alternate three- and four-day weeks. That is a five-hour commute involving car, airplane and train. Most people struggle with a commute of more than an hour.

Each morning when I open my eyes I say to myself:
"I, not events, have the power to make me happy
or unhappy today. I can choose which it shall be.
Yesterday is dead, tomorrow hasn't arrived yet. I have
just one day, today, and I'm going to be happy in it."
Groucho Marx

Use technology to benefit you

We talked earlier about the rise of the connected world. Let's now break it down a bit.

Brand building

Imagine being able to take a video of a patient seeing their new smile for the first time, upload it and let the world see their reaction before they have even got home to show their wife. What if this cost NOTHING? This is happening right now, thanks to the improved quality of video on smartphones and a free YouTube practice channel.

Gone are the days when you had to hire a video crew, lighting and editors, then burn onto DVD and send out to your patients one month later. There are two billion views of YouTube EVERY DAY; 24 hours of videos are uploaded every MINUTE. Google's automatic speech recognition software can change English to over 50 different languages, so it is truly global. Think of YouTube as a search engine; it is second only to Google.

So what videos can you upload?

- 'How to' videos—floss your teeth, use home whitening trays, treat mouth ulcers etc.

- 'Meet the team' videos—great way of building rapport.

- Video of your practice—but remember patients want to see beautiful surroundings with friendly team members. They DO NOT want to see your dental chair or suction machine, no matter how proud you are of them. They assume you have the latest equipment and it is well maintained. You can give this impression by showing the clean, comfortable and high tech patient areas and spare them the gory details.

- Media coverage—who's writing about you and why.

- Patient stories—what they say about you and your team. As I mentioned previously, your marketing message is much more powerful when it comes from patients.

Tip: when you video anyone, don't forget to ensure they sign a waiver so you can use their image and voice.

Did you know Facebook now has more internet traffic than Google?[22] People clearly want to connect and share stories. I only have a personal account and I have some patients who are friends. I do not have images of my kids or any incriminating pictures and I have set the security level to the highest so only my friends can view my images. I use it to show a glimpse of who James Goolnik is—my values, fun and interesting stuff that is going on in my life. I don't share what I had for dinner or when I visited the gym. It is brilliant at advertising events, courses, sharing pictures and videos with your global friends. You never need to forget a birthday again! I have had job offers and lots of patients wanting me to treat them. Facebook does give you an opportunity to show that dentists have their human side and it makes you more approachable.

Like any of these social media tools, you need to keep it up to date with relevant information and use the latest techniques. With Facebook advertising you can really target a micro-niche. You can choose female bankers in the 25-30 age bracket who work for Goldman Sachs, live in London and changed their relationship status from single to engaged. Then your advert appears for Goldman Sachs employees: 20% discount to have a white smile for your wedding day. You can hardly get more targeted than that. The great thing is you only pay when the advert is clicked on.

You can get a world class graphic designer to design your logo for less than $200 (£130). A great site I have used is Logo Tournament (www.logotournament.com) where you give a brief for your ideal logo and get designers to bid with their designs. You specify the style, concept, target audience, colour preference etc and then as they post the entries you rank them and add comments. They tweak the designs right up to the auction deadline. You then pay the winner and walk away with your new logo. It's a great business idea that fully harnesses the power of the internet in connecting people.

Once you have your logo it is important that it appears on all your marketing output and you have a consistent suite of material. So many times I see practices that have obviously spent a lot of money on marketing but still use old letterheads as they have loads left in stock. Sorry, it doesn't work like that. Throw the old stuff out. Everything from your business cards to your signage has to be on brand and on message.

Tracking supplies

With the economy as it is presently, dental practices are not ordering the same level of consumables as they used to. They rely on good systems to make sure they re-order, just in time. With the reliability of courier services now, there is little incentive to keep large stocks and you can free up capital and also space. Gone are the days when you bought a year's supplies of gloves to save money. With the transparency of the prices, customer loyalty is to the brand name of the product rather than the supply company. You can now log into your account to check the stock levels and the price of your consumables and some companies are even showing their competitors' prices alongside. The natural progression is to be able to track your order online, as you can do with FedEx for example, so you know exactly when it will be delivered.

I remember I was waiting for some toothpaste from the US and was getting frustrated that it had not arrived, despite having paid extra for expedited service. I called the company and was about to give them an earful when they told me it had been signed for by Dee at 10:15 that morning. I went to the front desk and Dee confirmed what they said. The parcel was on my desk!

Data Integration

Data is powerful and we use only a small percentage of what we have available to us. I can see us getting to a situation where we capture basic information only the once. Don't you just hate it when businesses ask repeatedly for information you have already given them? It can't be long before we have computer programs that talk to one another and use standardised fields to transfer data across platforms. Then team members will know where to look for the data they need and all people will need to do is to update the data as necessary.

One of the best new features on our clinical software is an instant messaging service, rather like group text messaging. You can send messages to a specific user, a group or the entire team; we have created a series of pre-written messages such as "I am finished with your patient. Are you ready?" in order to communicate better among the team.

Cloud computing

Why install software on all your office computers, pay for multiple licences and have the hassle of installing new updates regularly, when all the software you could ever need is on the internet? Cloud computing is a recent development whereby your computer applications run on a remote server and you access it securely via your internet connection. IT becomes a utility like electricity, and you only pay for what you use. The programs are always up to date, even your data is stored securely offsite and all you need are simple computers with tiny hard drives. Your team can access the same information from anywhere in the world, so your new patient coordinator does not need to be based in the same office or even the same town.

Come to think of it, with cloud-based systems your specialists could have access to all your patients' records, the same as you. Imagine your patients being able to visit the endodontist in another city and the endodontist having all the records, being able to write notes directly into the patient's file, update the post-operative X-rays and then rebook the patient back to see you for the crown preparation appointment. By 2012 it is predicted that 20% of businesses will own no IT assets.[23]

Data capture

Do you know how Facebook makes the majority of its revenue? No, not by advertising but by selling YOUR data. It sells information about where you live, what you like to eat, where you holiday and so on to companies that use it to target their products and services to you. Facebook updated its privacy policy and made all your profile information, comments, photos and activities public by default, unless you proactively go in and change your privacy settings.

As a dental practice, especially if you are fully computerised, you have a plethora of valuable information that you can use to better target your patients and even reach out to new ones. You could do an area search and plot where your patients live or work. You may find one company already has a high number of patients but you are not in contact with their HR people. Find out who is in charge of HR and give them a call to arrange a meeting. Tell them you already treat 30 people from their company who love your practice—how could you offer the same service to the rest of the company? Perhaps an employee benefit scheme with preferential members' rates?

Using all the data we already have, how can we better deliver our services? You can interrogate your records to see which times and days are most popular for hygiene appointments and use the information to decide which day to employ an extra hygienist.

Send birthday offers—how about a half-price dental hygiene visit in the week before your birthday? You already have some data about your patients such as date of birth and address. You should be capturing email addresses and, even more critical, mobile phone numbers. I am not sure about you, but I feel naked when I go out and leave my mobile phone at home. It is the best way to get in touch with a patient to remind them of their appointment and also to send offers. As with all contact, it needs not to be overdone and should be specifically targeted to the individual rather than a generic group.

With positioning devices now becoming standard on mobile phones, the possibilities are endless. Say it is 10am and you have just had a patient cancel a 3pm hygiene appointment with Sarah because they are sick. You should be able to interrogate your system to see who is overdue an appointment with Sarah, has their mobile phone switched on and is within a two-mile radius of your office. You could send a message to everyone who fits the criteria, and the first person replying to the message gets that appointment. If you want to add an incentive, give them 10% discount. Use your data intelligently, and empty appointment books should be a thing of the past.

With the merging of positioning devices, smartphones and Facebook we will see the advent of individually targeted advertising. Companies will know even more about our lives and be able to give a more personalised service. When you walk down the street the bill-boards will only show products that resonate with you.

Talking of smartphones, research by Gartner shows that by 2013 mobile phones will overtake PCs as the most common web access device worldwide. So how does your website look on a mobile? Have you made a slimmed-down mobile version that is easy to navigate on the smaller screen? Is it Flash-based and therefore not visible on an iPhone? You need to remove any possible barrier that might prevent a patient getting in touch. Can they book online? If not, why not? At the very least they need to be able to access you new patient form and complete the details from the comfort of their own home.

Brush strokes:

- How do you make it easy for your patients to afford your dental care?

- What are you passionate about?

- If you couldn't fail, what would you do?

- Update your Facebook privacy setting

- Look at ALL your marketing materials and practice stationery. Is it all on brand?

- Start capturing and using data smartly

- Take a look at your website on mobile devices like the Blackberry, iPhone and iPad

13 Don't forget to floss

Normal is not something to aspire to, it's something to get away from
Jodie Foster

So you've got there. You're where you wanted to be, and it wasn't as hard as you imagined. You overcame obstacles you didn't even dream about, and the ones you did dream about never materialised. What now?

CELEBRATE!

Most people forget to celebrate their successes and just keep looking for the next project. Take some time and acknowledge your journey and the people who have helped you on your way.

Foot on the gas

After you have celebrated, don't let the grass grow under your feet. It's all about momentum. Doors have opened and you are being offered opportunities. There are only two speeds in business: you either have your foot on the gas and are progressing, or you've taken your foot off and are coasting. Look in the mirror—they're starting to catch up again!

You may have read about the law of attraction: successful people like to surround themselves with similar people. I find that my patients who run successful innovative businesses enjoy spending time in other similar businesses such as mine. Look at the innovators in other industries. How can you create alliances with them? I have connections with dating coaches who run boot camps. I talk at their events on 'How to improve your confidence by improving your smile'. Some very successful people are not confident about their smile; they hold back as they are embarrassed. You may know some people like this. It is a win-win situation as we get to know about our patients and whether they are in relationships. We can refer people to help them on the path to finding a loving and honest relationship by meeting a relationship coach and finding out what they really want and why they have not found it yet.

We have talked a lot about innovation, but you can make a real difference just by looking at what your patients want. We found a good proportion of new patients who found us on the internet had trouble physically finding us on our street. The numbering system is a bit strange on Bow Lane. Just before I signed my contact with the landlord I noticed that the shop below us was also number 2. What did they do? Just wrote in an 'a' on the contract; now we are 2a. New patients are encouraged to download the iPhone app for free prior to their first appointment and it can direct them up to the door of our office whether they drive, walk or take the train.

What's new

With a few of my patients, the first thing they say at every recall appointment is "What's new?" We are known as innovators in dentistry and they love the fact we always have cool new stuff. Imagine Apple bringing out the iPod and then doing nothing to improve it for two years. It is the same in dentistry. Using patient feedback there are loads of small tweaks you can make to improve your customer service and treatment options. It could be just that you offer one late-night appointment session a week.

Remember it is all about your team. There is no point jumping on the bus, putting your foot on the gas and racing off to the next destination only to find you have left the rest of the team behind at the bus stop. You will find it is hard to do this stuff on your own and without team buy-in nothing will be permanent, just another of the boss's fads! Get them to experience your passion and enthusiasm for change and allow them the chance to ask why.

You're going to get copied

This is a biggie. Just as you are looking at the rest of the dental market and beyond, so are your competitors. If you bring out something new, you WILL get copied. If you are lucky they will change a bit, hopefully it's just the text in one of your ads. I cannot count how many times this has happened over the last ten years. If they are obviously plagiarising your work then I suggest you get in contact with them via email or letter and ask them to cease and desist prior to you taking further action. These are some of the ones that stand out for me:

a) Another dental website used an identical purple 'wave' as a header. The first day I noticed it, they even had the same names for their team members! They blamed the website developer but removed the site within 24 hours.

SHORTLY AFTER BOB WORE HIS 'DESIGNER' SHIRT WITH POCKET FOR HIS NEW iPAD, THE REST OF THE PRACTICE FOLLOWED SUIT

b) The dental price list of a practice around the corner from me was identical to mine, minus 10%. It had the exact same order of treatment and even had orthodontic fees when they did not have an orthodontist.

c) I pioneered Smiles for Life, the in-house bespoke patient membership scheme in the UK where patients pay a monthly fee for a certain level of service. A few weeks later they were springing up all over the country. Interestingly, they ALL included free tooth whitening.

d) Whitening Wednesdays. This was pioneered by a friend of mine, Daz Singh, where tooth whitening was half-price on Wednesdays. This has now sprung up all over the UK, including at Bow Lane!

Most of the time you can take it as flattery. Get over it and move on.

Top Brush tips

As time passes it will be harder to positively differentiate your practice by the physical environment and your treatment offerings. Having the latest gadget, reminder system, social networking and concierge-style service will be the norm. The gap between the great and the average will narrow. The below average will close. The one thing that will differentiate you from the competition is you and your team. The quality of the interaction with your patients is what sets you apart and really is all that matters. They are you best assets and you should treat them as such.

My number one tip is get them a copy of this book and make them feel appreciated. My other top tips are:

- Try it on a small scale, evaluate and then reset the course.
- Ask 'why' a lot, especially when someone says it cannot be done that way. They are often giving you responses based on the past.
- Remember about your core patients; use them as a focus group. They will love being involved and having their feedback valued.
- Listen to the newest member of your team. They are seeing your set-up with fresh eyes and are less likely to be jaded.
- The personal touch always wins.
- If you have made a mistake, say you are sorry and ask "What would it take to make you happy?" You will often be surprised by the response. If possible give your patients what they ask for.
- Measure what's important.
- Hire slowly, fire quickly.
- Crises create opportunities.
- Say "thank you" a lot.

This book is about being the most authentic dentist you can be; people will be attracted to your energy and you will love each second of your day. Shrug off that old white coat mindset and embrace the new you, the true you.

Have fun and keep polishing!

Contact me at www.jamesgoolnik.com

I would love to hear from you.

References

1. Lemelson-MIT Invention Index 2003
2. Alexander R. Stress-related suicide by dentists and other health care workers. JADA 2001;132(6): 786-794
3. O'Shea RM, Corah NL, Ayer WA. Sources of dentists' stress. JADA 1984;109(1): 48-51
4. ADA Survey of Current Issues in Dentistry 2007
5. ADA Survey of Dental Practice 2009
6. General Dental Council, Specialist List UK 2009
7. The Levin Group Practice Survey 2007
8. Dental Economics 2010
9. Van Haywood. Orthodontic Caries Control and Bleaching. *Inside Dentistry* April 2010 2-6
10. BACD Mintel Survey 2007
11. Dental Protection 2010
12. Google Insights 2010
13. Beall Research & Training of Chicago 2010
14. Adult Dental Heath Survey 2009
15. Simpson R, Beck J, Jakobsen J, Simpson J. Suicide statistics of dentists in Iowa, 1968 to 1980. JADA 1983;107(3): 441-3
16. BDTA Spotlight 2009
17. 2004 American Consumer Poll
18. Brahadeesh Chandrasekaran, Research Associate, Healthcare, EIA Jan 2011, The Rise of Cosmetic Dentistry
19. BACD Mintel Survey 2006
20. Hugh Flax
21. Align Technology 2008
22. Website Monitoring Stats 05/10
23. Gartner Survey 2010